Discovery EDUCATION | SCIENCE TECHBOOK

California

Volume 1

Unit 1: Objects Move and Collide

Unit 2: Moving Planets

To obtain permission(s) or for inquiries, submit a request to:
Discovery Education, Inc.
4350 Congress Street, Suite 700
Charlotte, NC 28209
800-323-9084
Education_Info@DiscoveryEd.com

ISBN 13: 978-1-68220-557-0

Printed in the United States of America.

9 10 11 12 13 14 15 16 CWM 27 26 25 24 23 22 C

Acknowledgments

Acknowledgment is given to photographers, artists, and agents for permission to feature their copyrighted material.

Cover and inside cover art: Sunti / Shutterstock

Letter to the Student

Dear Student,

See science in a whole new way! In this class, you'll be using California Science Techbook™. California Science Techbook is a science program developed by Discovery Education. The program is full of images, videos, Hands-On Activities, digital tools, reading passages, animations, and other activities. These resources will help you analyze and interpret data. You will solve problems and make connections between science and the world around you. California Science Techbook is made so you can work at your own pace and explore questions you may have about science. You'll even be able to see your progress in real time using the online Student Dashboard.

You will use this Student Edition to explore important ideas and record what you know and what you have learned. You'll also use it to make connections to the digital content in online Techbook. This will help you develop your own scientific understanding.

In each section of the Student Edition, you'll find QR codes. When you scan these codes, they'll take you to the online Science Techbook section you need. For instance, QR links throughout the book take you directly to important anchor or investigative phenomena videos and images. Once you are inside digital California Science Techbook, you can try some Explorations, Hands-On Activities, or Virtual Labs. All of them will help you explore the most important ideas in a concept. Enjoy this deep dive into the exciting world of science!

Sincerely,

The Discovery Education Science Team

Letter to the Parent/Guardian

Dear Parent/Guardian,

This year, your student will be using California Science Techbook™, a comprehensive science program developed by the educators and designers at Discovery Education.

California Science Techbook is an innovative program that offers engaging, real-world problems to help your student master key scientific concepts and act and think like a scientist. Students engage with interactive science instruction to analyze and interpret data, think critically, solve problems, and make connections across science disciplines. In addition, they experience dynamic content, explorations, videos, digital tools, Hands-On Activities and labs, and game-like activities that inspire and motivate scientific learning and curiosity.

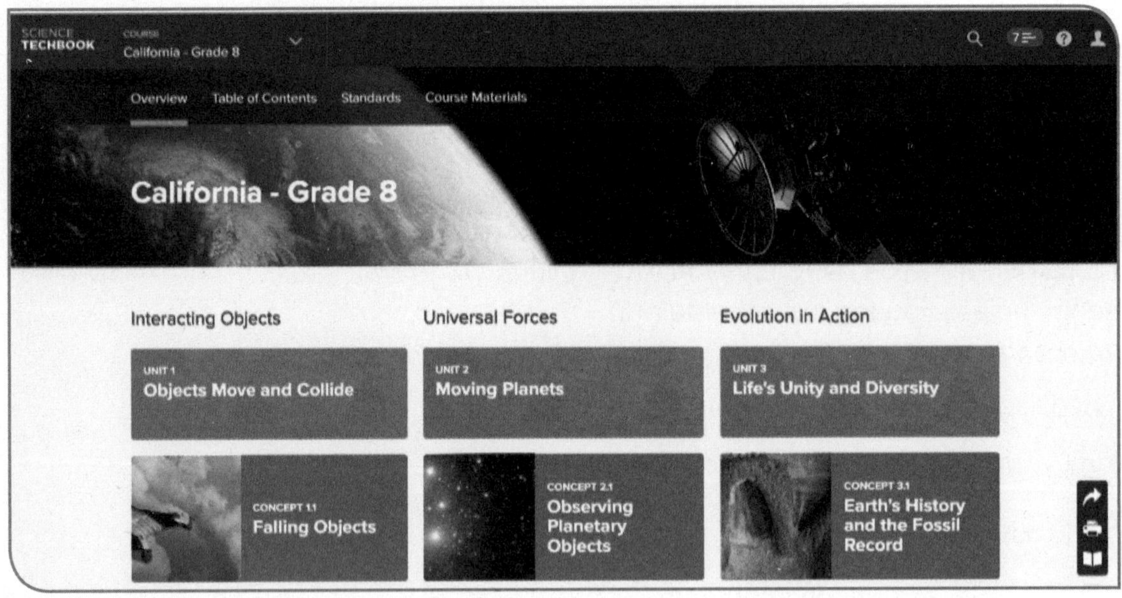

Discovery EDUCATION

Within this Student Edition, you'll find QR codes that take you and your student to a corresponding section of Science Techbook online. Once in Techbook, students will have access to the Core Interactive Text of each concept, as well as thousands of resources and activities that build deep conceptual scientific understanding. Additionally, tools and features such as the Interactive Glossary and text-to-speech functionality allow Science Techbook to target learning for students of a variety of abilities.

To use the QR codes, you'll need to download a free QR reader. Readers are available for phones, tablets, laptops, desktops, and virtually any device in between. Most use the device's camera, but there are some that scan documents that are on your screen.

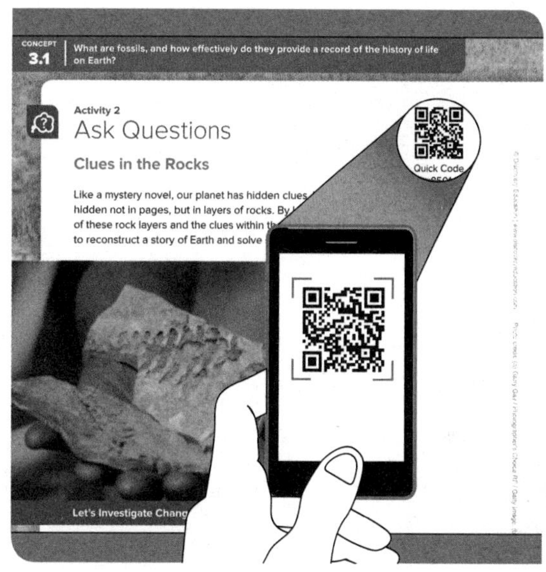

For resources in California Science Techbook, you'll need to sign in with your student's username and password the first time you access a QR code. After that, you won't need to sign in again, unless you log out or remain inactive for too long.

We encourage you to support your student in using California Science Techbook. May you and your student enjoy a fantastic year of science!

Sincerely,

The Discovery Education Science Team

Table of Contents

Unit 1: Objects Move and Collide

Unit Overview

Concept 1.1 Falling Objects

Concept 1.2 Energy for Launch

Concept 1.3 Colliding Objects

Unit Wrap-Up

Unit 2: Moving Planets

Unit Overview

Concept 2.1 Observing Planetary Objects

Concept 2.2 Planetary Forces

Concept 2.3 Orbital Forces

Concept 2.4 Energy in the Universe

Unit Wrap-Up

Resources

UNIT

1

Objects Move and Collide

Antarctica Impact Crater

Quick Code
ca8005s

Satellite technology discovered a strong gravitational pull coming from Antarctica. After investigating possible causes of the force, it was discovered that underneath the ice lies a large impact crater. An impact this size would have caused mass extinction of animals and sent waves of forces across the planet. At the end of the unit, you will be able to use the information you learned to describe the forces necessary to cause an impact crater of this size and identify other possible events that resulted from the impact.

Guiding Questions

1. What are forces, and how do they affect the motion of objects?
2. Do objects always need a force in order to keep moving?
3. What happens when a moving object collides with something?
4. How do fossils provide evidence of an ancient collision that wiped out the dinosaurs?

Gravity Anomaly in Antarctica: Crater Impact

Solve Problems

Quick Code
ca8006s

Unit Project: Prepare for Impact

Thinking About Solutions

Will humans have time to prepare for a large asteroid collision on Earth?

The Jet Propulsion Laboratory (JPL) has detected an asteroid headed toward Earth. You are a member of the Planetary Defense Coordination Office, and your job is to use the data gathered by the JPL to create a press release and inform the public about the incoming object.

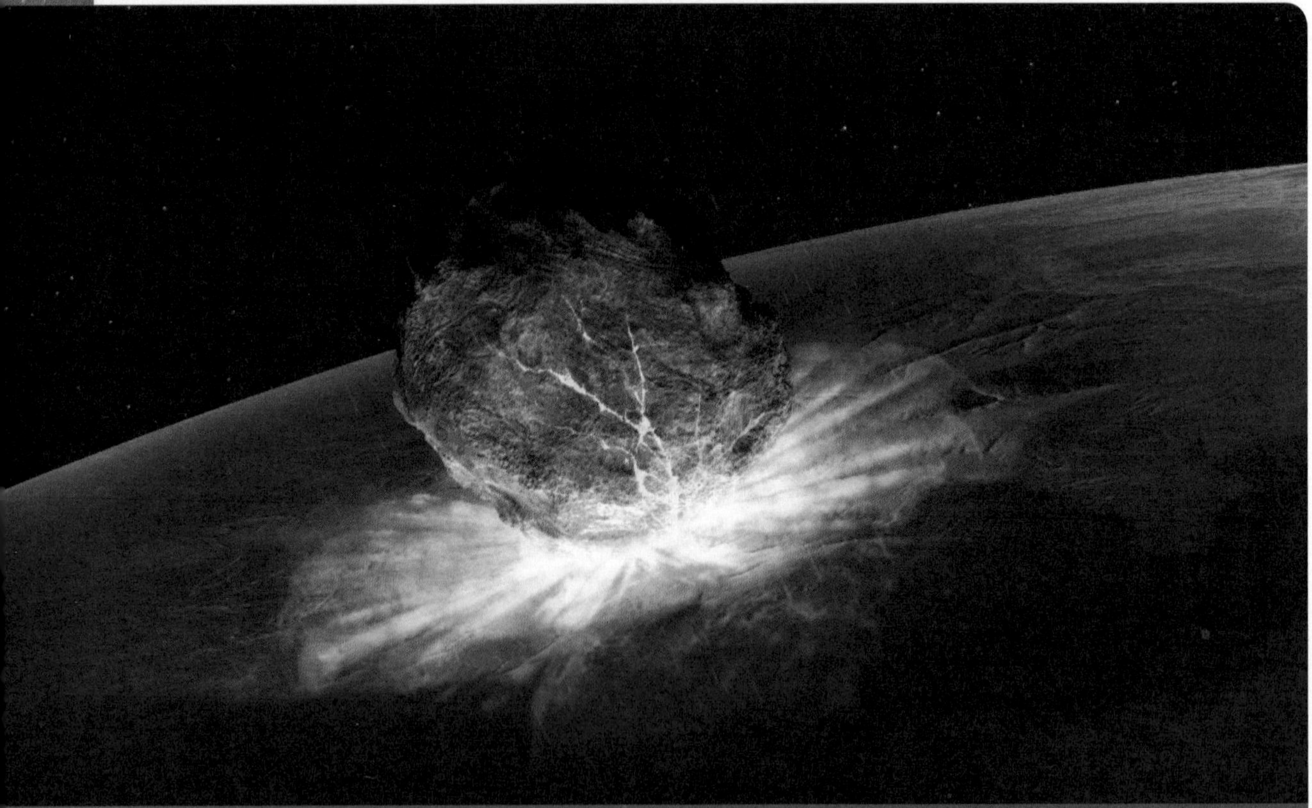

Asteroid Hitting Planet Earth

Use the graphic organizer to brainstorm your ideas.

What I Already Know

What I Need to Learn

CONCEPT

1.1

Falling Objects

Student Objectives

By the end of this lesson:

- [ ] I can obtain, evaluate, and communicate evidence to explain how an observer's frame of reference affects the apparent motion of an object.
- [ ] I can create a model that describes the forces acting on a free-falling object and that predicts the object's position and motion over time.
- [ ] I can construct graphs of the change of an object's position and motion over time and analyze the graphs to describe patterns in linear and nonlinear data sets.
- [ ] I can investigate and gather evidence to describe and predict how gravity causes objects to change their position and motion on small scales and planetary scales.
- [ ] I can develop models that describe friction as a force acting on an object and that predict how friction causes objects to change their position and motion.
- [ ] I can design, defend, and evaluate a solution to decrease kinetic friction acting on an airplane.

Key Vocabulary

acceleration, atmosphere, contact, Earth, force, frame of reference, friction, kinetic energy, kinetic friction, magnitude, mass, Newton's laws, orbit, potential energy, speed, surface, velocity, weight, work

Quick Code
ca8008s

Activity 1

Can You Explain?

Why do space objects fall to Earth?

Quick Code
ca8009s

Activity 2

Ask Questions

Quick Code
ca8010s

Satellites

With a group, **think** about and **discuss** the following claims:

- The distance from **Earth's** surface affects the velocity of a satellite.
- Satellites have different shapes of **orbit**.
- Satellites do not change altitude after they are placed into orbit.

Are these statements accurate? How do you know? As you watch the video, **write** evidence statements using information presented in the video. Each piece of evidence should be placed on a separate piece of paper. After generating your evidence statements, **place** each piece of evidence in the envelope with the claim that matches the evidence.

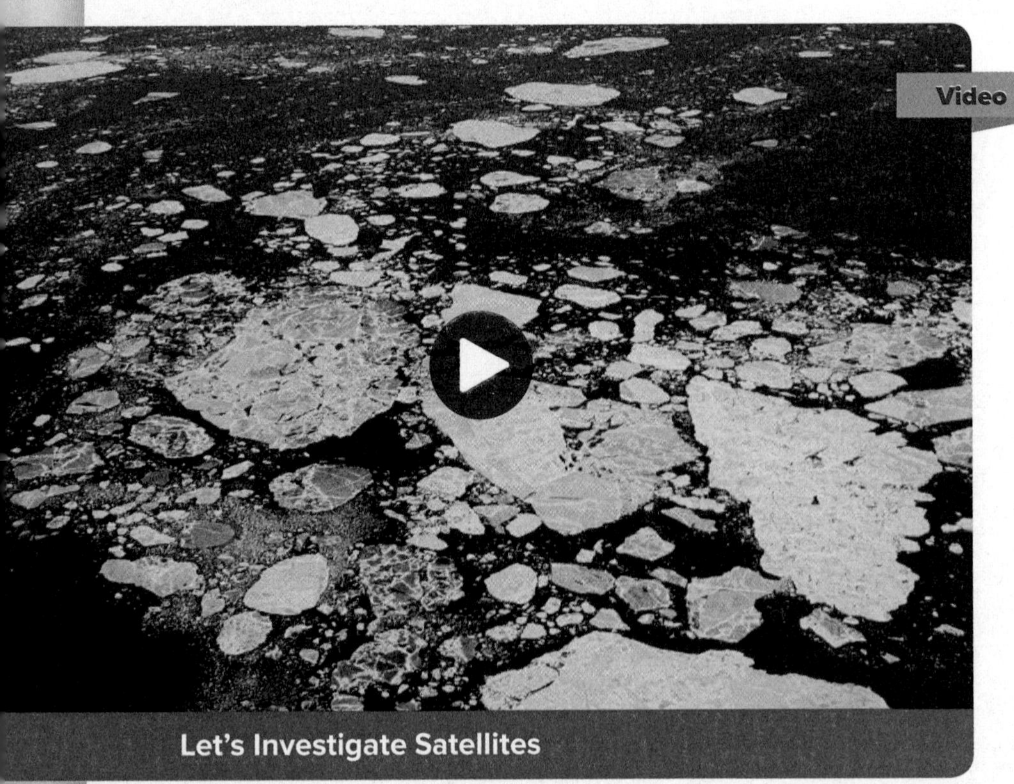

Video

Let's Investigate Satellites

ENGAGE

What questions do you have about satellites?

Activity 3

Analyze

Quick Code
ca8011s

Out-of-Orbit Satellites

Read the following text and **take a look** at the accompanying images and video. **Design** a model showing the motion of a satellite. **Include** labels that represent the mathematical data presented in the text.

Out-of-Orbit Satellites

Satellites are used for various purposes, ranging from communication and navigation to monitoring and collecting data. Most satellites used for scientific purposes have a low Earth orbit. Low Earth orbit is 160 to 2,000 kilometers above Earth's **surface**, just at the top of the **atmosphere**. The distance between Earth and the satellite determines the **velocity** of the orbit, as well as the gravitational **force** that is acting on the satellite. For example, a satellite that provides information to Global Positioning Systems (GPS) traveling at an altitude of 26,560 kilometers will take 12 hours to complete one orbit around Earth. A satellite traveling at a low Earth orbit of 705-kilometer altitude can travel at 27,500 kilometers per hour.

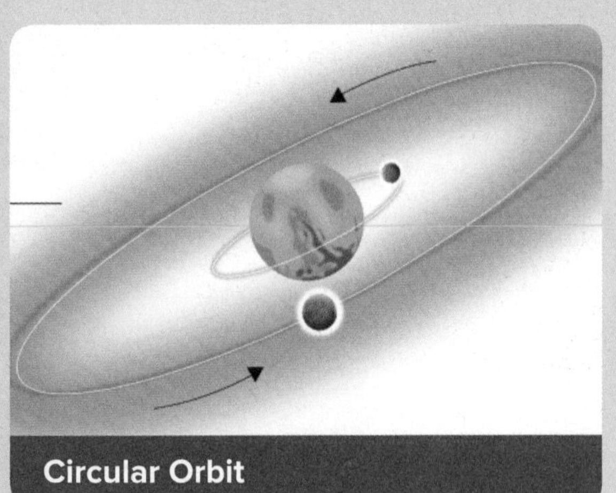

Circular Orbit

SEP **Developing and Using Models**

ENGAGE

Scientists and engineers use rockets to place satellites into orbit. Satellites can have circular orbits or elliptical orbits. In a circular orbit, the satellite travels at a constant **speed** and the satellite stays the same distance from the center of Earth.

In an elliptical orbit, a satellite travels in a path that is not a uniform distance from Earth's surface. At points where the satellite is closest to Earth's surface, the satellite will experience a greater gravitational pull from Earth. In an elliptical orbit, the satellite's velocity will increase as its height from Earth's surface decreases. The satellite's velocity will decrease as it moves in the orbit pathway farthest from the surface of Earth. What does a change in velocity indicate about the forces acting on the satellite?

Satellites in low Earth orbit are constantly being affected by gravity, atmospheric drag, and solar activity and will come down to Earth unless their orbits are adjusted. Satellites can also interact with other particles in low Earth orbit. More than 500,000 pieces of debris are orbiting Earth.

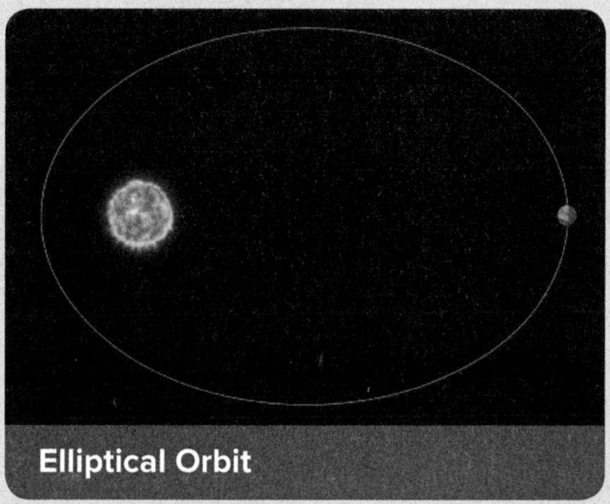

Elliptical Orbit

When this occurs, the satellite slows down and is overcome by the force of gravity, which pulls the satellite toward Earth. In most cases, as the satellite falls out of orbit, it will burn up in the atmosphere. In September 2011, a decommissioned NASA satellite fell back to Earth. The satellite broke apart upon entering the atmosphere and NASA estimates that 26 parts could have survived and landed in a remote location. NASA was unable to recover any remaining parts of the satellite.

Falling Satellites

Based on what you have read and seen, **design** a model showing the motion of a satellite. Include labels that represent the mathematical data presented in the text. **Draw** your model in the space provided.

Activity 4

Evaluate

Quick Code
ca8012s

What Do You Already Know About Falling Objects?

Tug-of-War

Consider a group of students playing a game of tug-of-war, in which two teams pull on a rope to find which team is strongest. Each of the statements that follows describes what happens during the tug-of-war. **Evaluate** each statement and **write** a check next to the statements that are accurate.

- ☐ If the rope does not move, the forces must be balanced.
- ☐ The team with the most people will always win the tug-of-war.
- ☐ The rope always accelerates in the direction of the greater force.
- ☐ The only force acting is the combined forces of the two teams pulling on the rope.

Forces and Motion

In a few sentences, **describe** motion and the forces that affect it. **Use** the chart to help organize your thoughts.

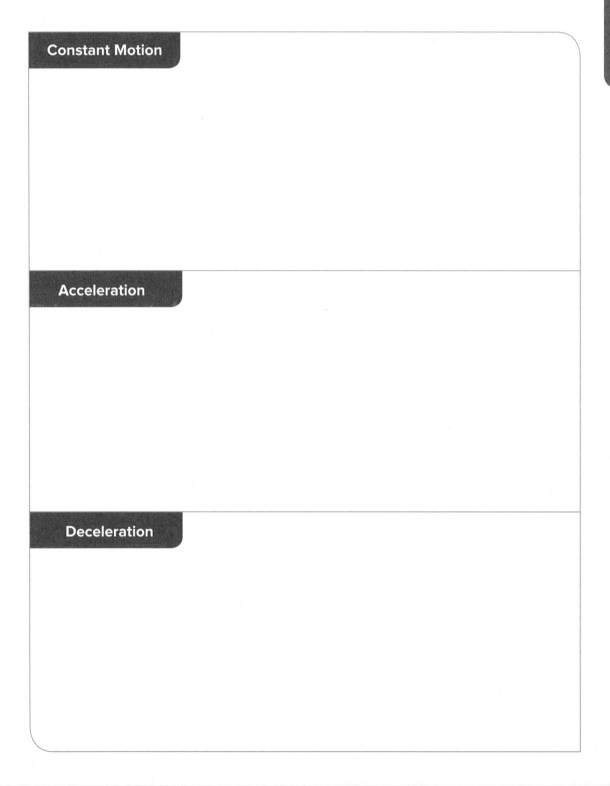

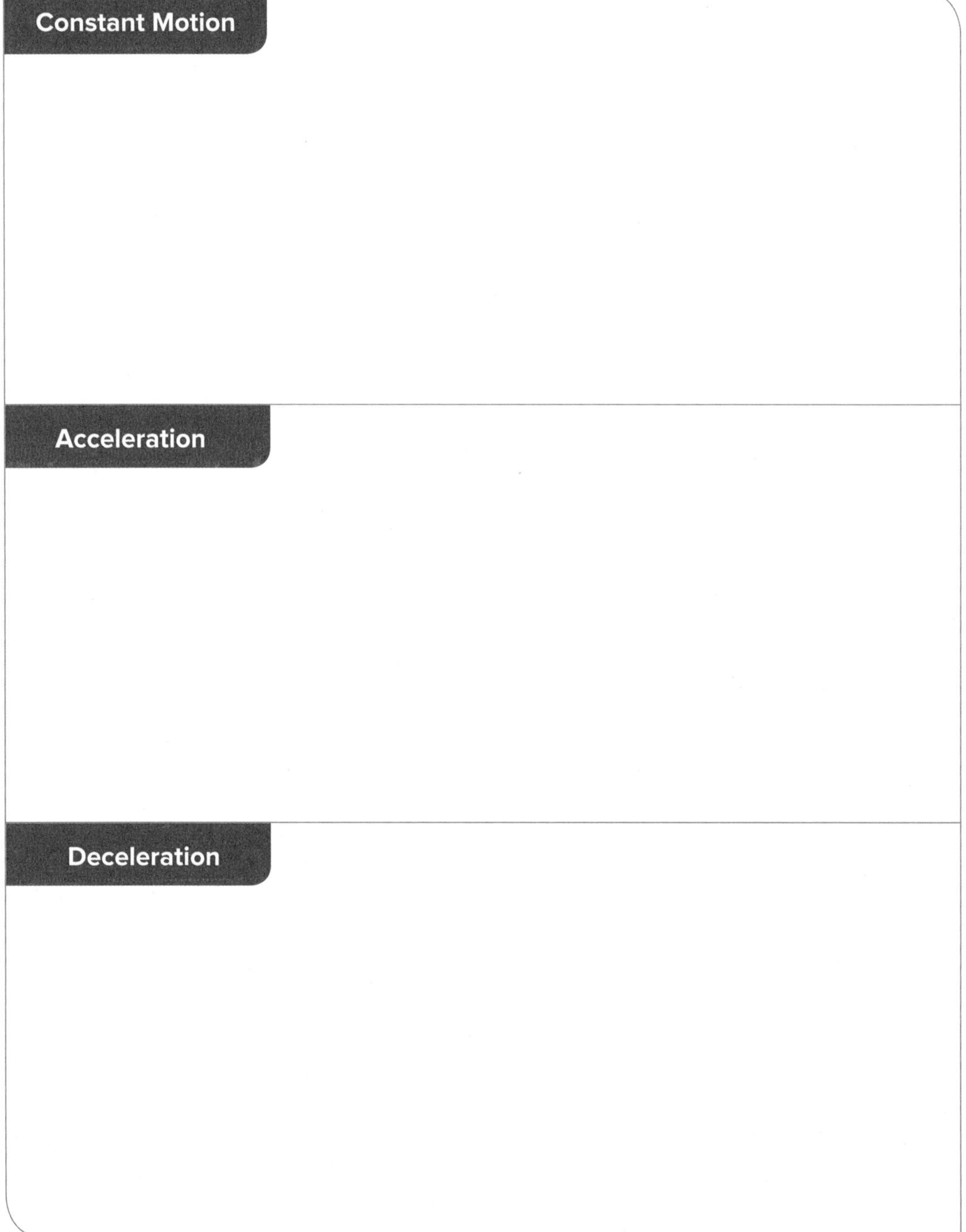

ENGAGE

Which statements correctly describe motion and forces that affect it? **Select** all of the statements that apply.

- ☐ The direction of an object's motion can be affected by only one force at a time.
- ☐ A single force can affect both the speed and the direction of an object's motion.
- ☐ A single force can cause the direction and speed of an object's motion to change.
- ☐ The direction of an object's motion is determined by the net force acting on it.
- ☐ An object falling toward Earth is being acted on only by gravity.
- ☐ *Velocity* is a scientific term for speed.
- ☐ An object that moves with constant speed always moves with constant velocity.
- ☐ An object's velocity is the distance it travels divided by the time taken to travel that distance.

Determining Direction of Motion

Explain the need for a reference point when describing the direction of motion. **Write** your response in the space provided.

ENGAGE

How Do We Describe the Motion of Objects Falling toward Earth?

Activity 5

Observe

Quick Code
ca8013s

Space Shuttle Test Flight

Watch the video Space Shuttle Test Flight, and pay close attention to what it teaches you about motion. During the second viewing, be ready to discuss parts of the video.

Space Shuttle Test Flight

SEP **Engaging in Argument from Evidence**

Next, **consider** the following claim: When the shuttle is removed from the transporting aircraft, its primary motion is in the vertical direction (toward Earth).

Is this claim correct? **Support** your response with evidence from the video. **Write** your response around the claim.

EXPLORE

As the shuttle is removed from the transporting aircraft, its primary motion is in the vertical direction (toward Earth).

Activity 6

Observe

On the Move

Quick Code
ca8014s

You will complete two activities that define the term *frame of reference*. The first activity will be the Interactive On the Move, which explores motion. The next activity requires you to read some text that describes frame of reference.

As you complete these two activities, **evaluate** the advantages and disadvantages of defining the term through two different mediums.

Go online to complete the activity On the Move. **Record** your notes in the data chart.

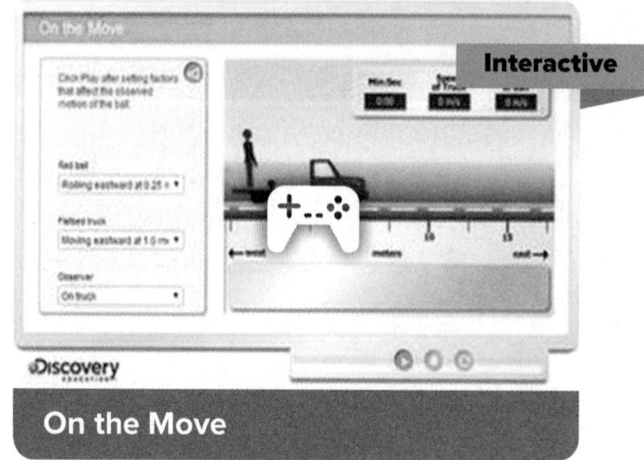

On the Move

CCC Scale, Proportion, and Quantity

Record the results of the Interactive in the data table.

		Distance Ball Moved	
Red Ball	**Flatbed Truck**	**Observer on Truck**	**Observer Not on Truck**
Rolling eastward at 0.25 m/s	Rolling eastward at 1.0 m/s		
	Accelerating eastward at 0.2 m/s		
Rolling westward at 0.25 m/s	Rolling eastward at 1.0 m/s		
	Accelerating eastward at 0.2 m/s		

EXPLORE

Activity 7
Analyze

Quick Code
ca8015s

Frame of Reference

Read the following text. As you read, **think** about what you learned in the Interactive. Then, **answer** the question that follows.

Frame of Reference

Have you ever flown in an airplane? When you look up to the sky and observe airplanes flying, you may notice the airplane traveling at fast speeds across the sky. The origin point of the airplane's flight is an airport. For passengers inside the airplane, as they descend closer to the ground as they come in for a landing, they observe objects moving across their view through the window. The passengers may say that objects such as trees and other landmarks are moving, not the plane.

The **frame of reference** is the point from which the investigator is observing an object's motion. This is important because the motion can appear quite different depending on the reference frame being used. For example, suppose a child is on a train moving out of a station. The child is holding an ice cream cone. To the child, the ice cream cone is not moving. However, if you were standing on the station platform watching the train pull out, you would see the ice cream cone moving as the train moved. The same object, the ice cream cone, is viewed as having different motions from the two reference frames. Both are correct descriptions of motion.

Now that you have completed the Interactive and read the text, **think** about what you learned each time. Which method of presentation helped you better understand the meaning of the term *frame of reference*? **Write** your thoughts in the space provided.

EXPLORE

Activity 8

Analyze

Quick Code
ca8016s

Change of Position over Time

Read the text and **look** for examples of motion.

Change of Position over Time

When describing motion, it is important to determine the proper frame of reference for the system you are investigating. Consider an airplane passenger throwing a ball in the air. If we wanted to analyze the motion of the ball, should we consider the interior of the plane our frame of reference, or the surface of Earth as our frame of reference? We want to select a frame of reference that allows our origin point to be a point that is not moving. However, both the interior of the plane and a point on Earth's surface are actually moving.

In order to use predictable patterns of motion to analyze the motion of objects, ideally, we want to use the frame of the stars. The frame of the stars means that if you were sitting on a star, what would you observe as the change in the object's position? This may be difficult to measure. Therefore, a local frame of reference is needed to analyze an object's motion. The local frame of reference should move with a constant velocity in a straight line or rotate at a constant rate around a fixed point. If those conditions are met, we are able to apply Newton's laws to predict and describe the motion of objects. In the case of the passenger throwing the ball in the air, one can select the interior of the airplane if the airplane is traveling at constant velocity.

CCC **Scale, Proportion, and Quantity**

Earth spins at a constant rate around a fixed point. When analyzing the motion of a book being pushed across a desk, an appropriate frame of reference would be the tabletop, as it is a fixed horizontal surface the book is traveling along. The change in position of the book can be measured from the point of origin along the horizontal surface. A local frame of reference can be thought of as a coordinate system. How does the object change its position over time in the x- and y-direction? Once you determine and communicate the frame of reference, you can begin to quantify and measure the motion of the object.

An object at rest will stay at rest until acted upon by a force. When an object is at rest, the object possesses **potential energy**. When in motion, the potential energy of the object is converted to **kinetic energy**. Consider someone carrying a watermelon to the top of a building. As the person carries the watermelon, he is adding gravitational potential energy to the watermelon. As the watermelon sits on the top of the building, it has maximum potential energy. As soon as the person adds a force to push the watermelon off of the building, the potential energy is converted to kinetic energy.

A frame of reference is useful to describe the motion and change in energy of the watermelon. For example, when dropping the watermelon from the rooftop, the point of origin can be the top of the building or the ground. One would represent the change in motion, in relation to the origin point. In free fall, the force acting upon an object is gravity. We do not consider air resistance for objects in free fall; therefore, the **mass** and shape of the object do not affect the motion of the object.

EXPLORE

Based on the text, what are some examples of motion? Include the examples you found and describe an accurate frame of reference for one example. Then, describe an inappropriate frame of reference for that example.

Examples of Motion	
Appropriate Frame of Reference for One Example	**Inappropriate Frame of Reference for One Example**

Answer the following questions.

Which frame of reference would work best to describe the example(s) of motion?

EXPLORE

Describe an inappropriate frame of reference. Why is this scale not appropriate for describing the example(s) of motion?

Activity 9

Interpret Data

Quick Code
ca8017s

Free-Falling Data

Analyze the data in Table 1.

Table 1. Data Representing the Motion of a Free-Falling Object

Time (seconds)	0	1	2	3	4	5	6	7	8
Distance (meters)	0	4.9	19.6	44.1	78.4	122.5	176.4	240.1	313.6

EXPLORE

If Table 1 represents the change in position over time of a watermelon dropped from a building, which frame of reference was used to create the data? **Write** your response in the space provided.

SEP Analyzing and Interpreting Data

Activity 10

Investigate

Quick Code
ca8018s

Hands-On Investigation: Frame of Reference

In this investigation, you will explore how your frame of reference affects the way that you interpret an object's movement.

Predict

How do you predict motion will change depending on where you stand?

SEP Planning and Carrying Out Investigations

CCC Scale, Proportion, and Quantity

What materials do you need? (per group)

- Newton's cradle
- Beach ball, Earth
- Round sticker in bright color
- Cart or chair with wheels
- Stopwatch
- Measuring tape

EXPLORE

Procedure

1. Attach the sticker to the top of the ball or wheel so that the sticker dot can be seen from the side.
2. Roll the ball, observe what happens, and draw the action.
3. Write and draw your observations.

Next, trade drawings with another group. What is similar about the drawings?

____

____

____

____

What is different?

Can you design an experiment that will help you determine how frame of reference changes with position? Describe your experiment.

What objective data could you gather in this experiment?

Reflect

Were you surprised at your results? Explain.

What other questions do you have about the effect of frame of reference on an object's motion?

Consider space exploration and astronomy. How does frame of reference help or hinder the study of space from Earth? What is a solution?

EXPLORE

What Forces Act on Objects Falling toward Earth?

Activity 11

Investigate

Quick Code
ca8019s

Hands-On Investigation: Free Fall

In groups, complete the following activity and record your results in your notebook. Then, switch notebooks with another group and analyze others' procedures. Be sure to provide feedback.

In this investigation, you will explore Newton's second law of motion by investigating the motion of an object on which gravity is acting as a force.

Predict

How do you predict gravity will affect the motion of objects?

SEP Planning and Carrying Out Investigations

SEP Analyzing and Interpreting Data

What materials do you need? (per group)

- Stopwatch
- Measuring tape
- Tennis balls
- Calculator, battery-powered
- Digital video camera (optional)
- Balance, triple beam
- Spring scale
- Hooked weight (extension activity)
- Computer access (extension activity)

EXPLORE

Procedure

1. Design a test in which you measure how far the ball travels to record distance over time for several heights.
2. In the space provided, create a data table in which you can record the measurements from multiple trials.
3. Carry out your investigation and record the data in your data table.

Distance	Trial	Times (s)	Average Time (s)	Average Veocity (m/s)	Average Acceleration (m/s^2)

Reflect

How did the average speed of a tennis ball dropped a short distance compare with the average speed of a tennis ball dropped a long distance? (Remember that average speed can be calculated by dividing the total distance traveled by the total time.)

Imagine that a tennis ball is dropped from a tall building. If it falls 5 meters in the first second after it is dropped, will it fall 5 meters, more than 5 meters, or less than 5 meters in the next second? What can you predict about how far it will fall in the second after that? (Assume that the only force acting on the ball is gravity.) Explain your answer.

To calculate the acceleration of an object dropped from rest, you can use the equation $a = \frac{2d}{t^2}$, where *a* is acceleration, *d* is distance traveled, and *t* is the time required to travel the distance. On Earth, acceleration due to gravity is 9.8 meters per second squared. How does the calculated acceleration of the tennis ball in your investigation compare with the true acceleration due to gravity? What factors might have affected the accuracy of your measurements? What variables might not have been controlled?

Activity 12

Analyze

Quick Code
ca8020s

Gravity

As you read the text, **underline** or **highlight** details about force and force diagrams.

EXPLORE

Gravity

Forces have both a **magnitude**, or strength, and a direction. You can create diagrams showing forces acting on objects. Such diagrams can be useful in evaluating how an object will be affected by several forces acting on it at once. Each force is drawn as an arrow with a length and a direction. The length represents the magnitude of the force. The arrow points in the direction the force is acting.

One consistent force acting upon objects is the gravitational force between Earth and other objects. You are aware of this force every time you drop something and it falls to the floor. Another force is **friction**, which is a force that resists motion when two objects rub together.

You may have heard of objects falling down to the ground as objects in free fall. Free fall indicates that no external forces are acting on the object, except for gravity. In reality, only in a vacuum is an object in free fall, as gravity is the only force acting upon the object. An object falling back to Earth's **surface** through the **atmosphere** is acted upon by the force of gravity, but also encounters a drag force, which can be considered aerodynamic friction. The molecules of air move against the surface of the falling object. This interaction of surfaces results in an upward frictional force.

Using what you have read, **construct** a force diagram for the tennis ball you tested in the activity Free Fall.

Activity 13

Investigate

Quick Code
ca8021s

Hands-On Investigation: Mass and Gravity

In this investigation, you will attempt to scientifically prove Newton's law of universal gravitation.

Predict

Will mass affect the average rate of fall of an object due to gravity?

EXPLORE

SEP Planning and Carrying Out Investigations

SEP Using Mathematics and Computational Thinking

What materials do you need? (per group)

- Whiffle balls
- Modeling clay
- Tennis balls
- Stopwatch
- Masking tape

Procedure

1. Design a test in which you determine if mass affects the speed in which an object falls.
2. Record your procedure in the space provided.

Carry out your investigation and record the data in the data table.

	Hollow Ball			Clay Ball			Tennis Ball		
	1	2	3	1	2	3	1	2	3
Time (s)									
Average Velocity (m/s)									
Average Acceleration (m/s^2)									

Reflect

Were you surprised by your results? Explain.

What other questions do you have about the effect of gravity on objects?

EXPLORE

Consider the International Space Station (ISS). The mass of the ISS is 419,455 kilograms. How do you think your data compares with the effects of gravity on much more massive objects like this one?

Reflect on your data. Use it to predict the average rate of fall for the ISS.

Activity 14
Analyze

Quick Code
ca8022s

Friction

Read the following text.

Then, on sheets of construction paper, **design** a model of the system you tested in the activity Mass and Gravity. Your model should indicate the inputs, processes, and outputs of the system, as well as the places in the system where the different masses have maximum potential energy and maximum kinetic energy. **Use** the chart to organize your thoughts.

EXPLORE

Friction

You may have learned about conservation of energy and energy transfer related to changes in states of matter. Energy is also transferred in systems such as cellular respiration. For objects in motion, conservation of energy and transfer of energy also applies. Potential energy of an object describes the ability of an object to do **work**. All objects have energy stored as potential energy in their resting state. Gravitational potential energy is perhaps the most common potential energy we experience in our daily lives. This is the energy stored in an object that has been lifted up against the force of gravity. When gravitational potential energy is released, the force of gravity does the work to move a mass down toward Earth's surface.

SEP Developing and Using Models

CCC Systems and System Models

Friction *cont'd*

If all of the potential energy of an object is converted to kinetic energy, why does an object stop moving? If the object did not interact with any other objects, as it moves in the air or across a surface, it would continue moving in the same direction. However, we already know that when an object moves across a surface or through the air, it experiences the force of friction, counteracting the direction of motion.

Before the Drop:	**After the Drop:**
During the Drop:	

In groups, **share** your models and **exchange** feedback. **Revise** your model based on the feedback.

EXPLORE

Activity 15

Record Evidence

Quick Code
ca8023s

Satellites

As you worked through this lesson, you investigated and gathered evidence about falling objects. Now, take another look at the video Satellites, which you first saw in Engage.

How has your understanding of Satellites changed?

Read the Can You Explain? question from the beginning of this lesson.

Can You Explain?

Why do space objects fall to Earth?

SEP Constructing Explanations and Designing Solutions

Plan a scientific explanation to answer the Can You Explain? or a question of your own. Recall that a scientific explanation contains three elements: a scientific claim, evidence to support the claim, and reasoning that connects the evidence to the claim. Use this planning chart to develop your scientific explanation:

Scientific Explanation Planning Chart
What is my claim?
What data from my investigations can I use to support my claim?
What reliable evidence from the text and/or videos can I use as evidence?

EXPLAIN

What reliable evidence from the text and/or videos can I use as evidence?

Which scientific ideas, principles, and/or laws apply to my explanation?

Now, **use** the information in your planning chart to **write** your scientific explanation.

Scientific Explanation (Explanation = Claim + Evidence + Logical Reasoning)	
Directions:	Key Components:
Create a scientific explanation for the question. This combines the claim that was made, the evidence that was collected, and a justification for why the evidence supports the claim (logical reasoning). The explanation should contain clear thoughts and accurate scientific vocabulary.	• Uses precise and accurate language • Uses scientific vocabulary • Provides clear, logical thoughts • Uses evidence and reasoning to support the claim

EXPLAIN

STEM in Action

Activity 16

Analyze

Quick Code
ca8024s

Heat Shields on Rocket Ships

Read the text and **look** for examples of beneficial heat and friction. Then, **complete** the activities that follow.

Heat Shields on Rocket Ships

Friction sometimes can have the effect of slowing down objects or keeping them from sliding around. However, friction also causes things to heat up. For example, think about how hot your hands become when you rub them together. This happens because of the friction forming between your palms as they slide against each other. Now, think about what would happen if you could rub your hands together 25 times faster than the speed of sound. The kind of heat generated by that much friction is something that NASA engineers must consider when a space vehicle reenters Earth's atmosphere after a trip to space.

When a space shuttle reenters Earth's atmosphere, it could be traveling at 18,000 miles per hour. The atmosphere acts as a frictional drag force on the shuttle. This is similar to the way water exerts a drag force on a swimmer diving into a pool. However, the frictional force between the spaceship and the air generates heat.

SEP Constructing Explanations and Designing Solutions

So much heat is produced that the air surrounding the ship can no longer exist as a gas.

The gas becomes a high-energy plasma like the sun. Plasmas are a fourth phase of matter different from solids, liquids, and gases. In fact, the temperature surrounding a spaceship on reentry can reach nearly 3,000°F!

Engineers who design these spaceships must use materials that can withstand high temperatures and protect the crew inside. This means that the materials cannot conduct any of the heat that they are exposed to. NASA engineers have developed porous ceramic tiles to cover the ship's entry side. These tiles are light and resistant to heat. The tiles are coated with a black glassy liquid to prevent the hot plasma from sticking to the tiles.

The part of the ship that enters the atmosphere head-on has the hottest temperatures. At these temperatures, the ceramic tiles on the rest of the ship would break apart. For this special zone, NASA engineers developed a material called reinforced carbon-carbon to provide additional protection. The drawback to this material is that it is heavy, so the whole ship cannot be lined with it.

As new spacecraft are designed and built, engineers must continue to develop materials and solutions to the dangers of friction during reentry.

How could you engineer a device that produces beneficial friction and heat? **Write** your response.

Friction: Friend or Foe?

For NASA engineers, the heat created by the friction between a spacecraft and Earth's atmosphere is bad. However, there are some situations in which scientists and engineers might want the heat produced by friction in a machine.

Think of one example where heat and friction are good outcomes of a process or machine. **Identify** the specific cause of friction in this process and the object(s) that becomes hotter as a result. **Use** the Cause/Effect chart to organize your ideas.

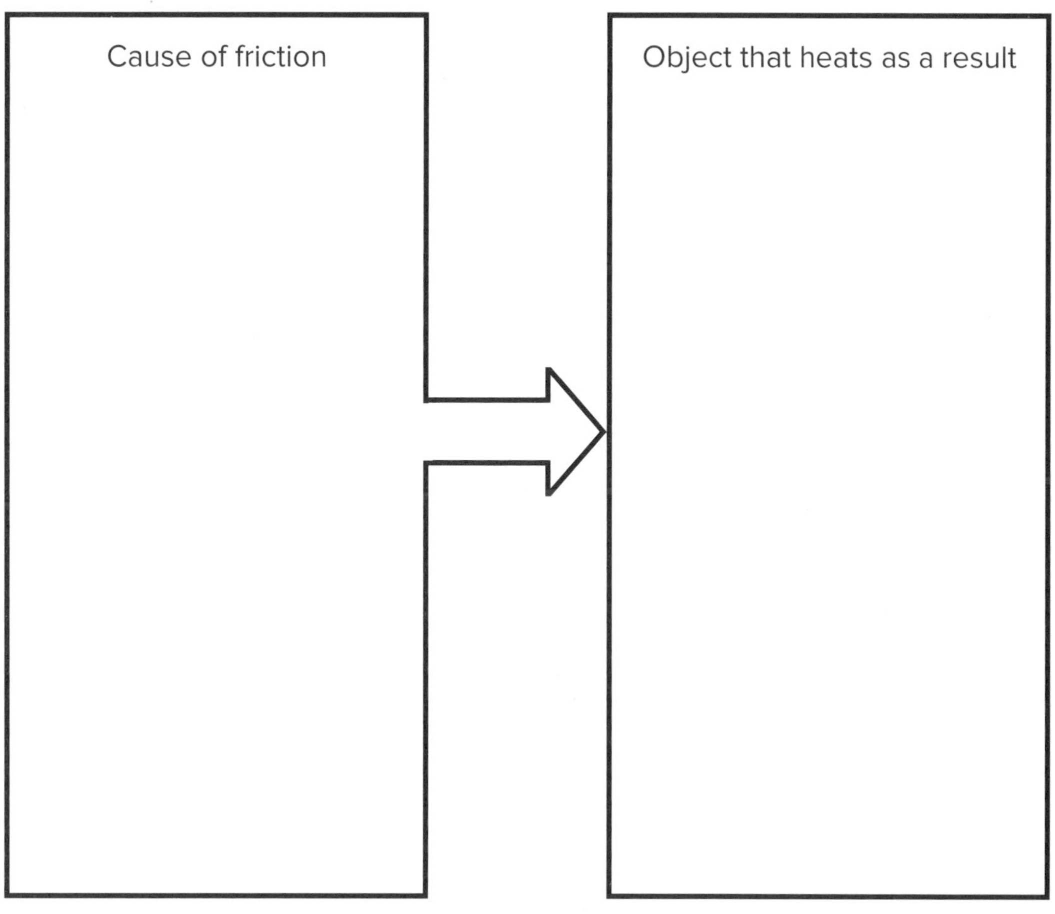

Describe how you could engineer the situation to produce even more friction and heat.

ELABORATE

Activity 17

Concept Review

Review: Falling Objects

Quick Code
ca8025s

Now that you have completed the objectives for this concept, **review** the core ideas you have learned. Record some of the core ideas in the space provided.

Core Ideas

Talk with a Group

Now, think about the asteroid impact crater video you saw in Get Started. Discuss how what you've learned about falling objects can help you understand an asteroid colliding with Earth.

EVALUATE

CONCEPT

1.2

Energy for Launch

Student Objectives

By the end of this lesson:

- [ ] I can design and carry out investigations to collect and analyze data that describe and predict the effect of an object's mass on its changing position and motion.
- [ ] I can develop a model that describes the relationships among speed, force, mass, and acceleration and that predicts how a change to one factor affects the other factors.
- [ ] I can synthesize information from a variety of scenarios that reinforce Newton's third law.
- [ ] I can design and carry out investigations to collect and analyze data that describe the linear relationship between the mass of an object and the force required to move the object and to predict the effect of a change in one variable on the other.
- [ ] I can develop models that describe patterns in energy transfer and conservation in systems involving objects in motion.
- [ ] I can argue from evidence that an increase in velocity of an object in motion results in an increase of kinetic energy.
- [ ] I can use mathematics and computational thinking to calculate acceleration at various points along a rocket's trajectory.

Key Vocabulary

acceleration, conservation of energy, density, force, gravity, hydrogen, magnitude, mass, measure, motion, orbit, oxygen, potential energy, speed, system, thrust, velocity, weight

Quick Code
ca8027s

Activity 1

Can You Explain?

How do mass and energy affect the acceleration of a rocket?

Quick Code
ca8028s

Activity 2

Ask Questions

Quick Code
ca8029s

Rockets

How is a rocket different from an airplane? The obvious difference is the shape of the vehicle, as well as the **motion** of the vehicle. An airplane travels across the sky, while a rocket propels itself in a vertical direction. You may not recognize another difference. An airplane uses its jet engines to mix air with fuel and burn it for forward motion. A rocket carries its entire fuel supply onboard.

Let's Investigate Rockets

What questions do you have about rockets?

____

____

____

Massive Amateur Rocket

Watch this video about the forces acting on a rocket.

After you have watched the video, **think** about how you would create force diagrams for each phase of the rocket's travels.

What questions do you have about forces acting on rockets?

ENGAGE

Create a force diagram depicting the forces acting on the rocket from the video. Be sure to show changes in the magnitude of forces in each diagram. You will draw diagrams for each of the following phases:

At the beginning of the launch:

Halfway through the ascent:

Halfway through the descent:

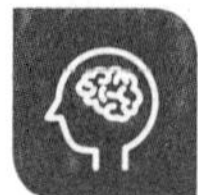

Activity 3

Evaluate

Quick Code
ca8030s

What Do You Already Know About Energy for Launch?

Identifying Forces 1

Study the scenarios described in the diagram that follows. For each one, **write** the types of forces acting on the object next to the correct arrows in the diagram. **Choose** the forces from the list:

- applied force
- gravity
- air resistance
- friction
- normal force

Scenario	Force Applied
A box is being pushed to the left.	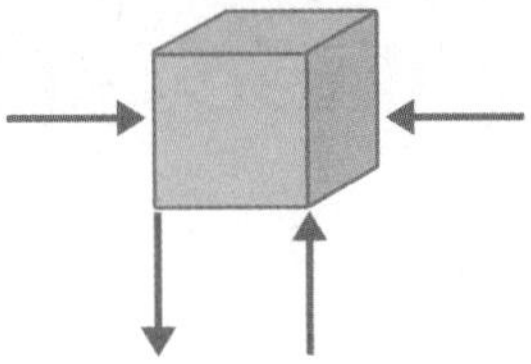
A penny falls through the air.	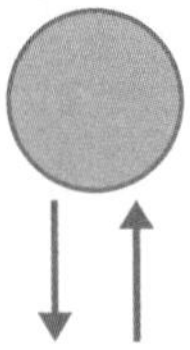
A ball flies up into the air.	
A person stands at rest on the ground.	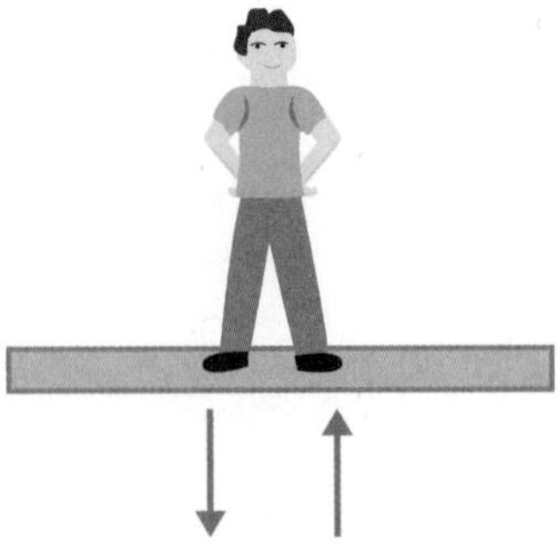

Force, Motion, and Flight

Read the following statements about force, motion, and flight. **Select** all that are true.

- ☐ If a flying object speeds up, the forces acting on it are unbalanced.
- ☐ When forces are balanced, a flying object stops moving.
- ☐ If you throw a paper airplane, a force is acting on it until it lands.
- ☐ A paper airplane eventually slows down because of drag, or resistance from the air.
- ☐ Unbalanced forces are required to get a plane moving from rest.

ENGAGE

Comparing Terms and Velocity and Acceleration

Complete a Vocabulary Chart for each of the terms: *speed*, *velocity*, and *acceleration*. Then, complete the activities.

Definition
- **Personal:**
- **Dictionary:**

Examples (drawn or written)

speed

Sentences
- **Teacher/Book:**
- **Personal:**

Related:

Word Parts:

ENGAGE

Definition
- **Personal:**
- **Dictionary:**

Examples (drawn or written)

velocity

Sentences
- **Teacher/Book:**
- **Personal:**

Related:

Word Parts:

Definition
- **Personal:**
- **Dictionary:**

Examples (drawn or written)

acceleration

Sentences
- **Teacher/Book:**
- **Personal:**

Related:

Word Parts:

Which statements correctly compare the meaning of the terms *speed* and *velocity*? Check all that apply.

- [ ] Velocity is just a more scientific word for speed.
- [ ] Both terms describe how fast an object is moving.
- [ ] Only velocity also describes the direction of an object.
- [ ] Only speed can be used if an object is moving at a constant rate.
- [ ] Most of the time the terms can be used interchangeably.

Which statement uses the terms *velocity* and *acceleration* correctly?

- ☐ Acceleration is the rate of change of velocity.
- ☐ An object with a constant velocity cannot accelerate.
- ☐ Acceleration is always in a straight line.
- ☐ Acceleration is an increase in velocity.
- ☐ Acceleration happens only in the same direction as the object is moving.

How Much Force and Energy Do We Need to Launch a Rocket?

Activity 4

Observe

Quick Code
ca8031s

Apollo Rocket

Review the image. **Draw** and **label** a diagram showing the forces that are acting on the launchpad and the forces acting on the rocket in the image.

Apollo Rocket

Draw your force diagrams here.

EXPLORE

Activity 5

Investigate

Quick Code ca8032s

Hands-On Investigation: Marble Madness

In this activity, you will demonstrate how unbalanced forces and the mass of an object affect the speed and direction of the object's motion.

Predict

How will unbalanced forces affect the speed and direction of an object?

SEP **Using Mathematics and Computational Thinking**

What materials do you need? (per group)

- Marbles, $\frac{5}{8}$ in.
- Hardback textbooks, 4
- Metric ruler
- Plastic straws
- Safety goggles (per student)
- Marbles, 1 in.

EXPLORE

Procedure

Part 1: The Effect of Forces on Motion

Place a marble on the table. Draw a diagram of the forces acting on the marble when it is at rest.

Blow air on the marble through a straw until it moves. Draw a diagram of the forces acting on the marble now. Label these forces “balanced” or “unbalanced.”

Now, blow air on the marble, but do NOT make the marble move. Diagram the forces that are acting on the marble now.

Place the marble on a stack of books so that it experiences first balanced, then unbalanced, forces. Diagram what happens each time, and label the forces.

Part 2: The Effect of Mass and Motion

Place both marbles on a desk. Draw a diagram that shows all of the forces acting upon the marbles. Label the diagram as showing balanced or unbalanced forces on each marble.

EXPLORE

Plan how you will collect evidence that shows how a change in motion relates to both the force acted upon the object and the mass of the object. Finally, place the marbles on the stack of books so that only one of the marbles experiences balanced forces (one marble moves while the other stays in place). Create this diagram, labeling the forces and indicating which marble moved and which one did not.

Reflect

What new information did you learn about the relationship between unbalanced forces, speed, and direction?

Think about the activity you just completed. Describe how an object might be affected with more than one unbalanced force acting upon it.

What did you do to the textbooks to cause unbalanced forces to act upon the marble? In this case, what forces caused the speed or direction of the marble to change?

Does applying the same force to marbles with different masses result in the same motion? Explain why or why not.

Which marble moved more as a result of blowing air on it? Describe how mass might affect the amount of force needed to cause motion across a table.

EXPLORE

Which marble moved more as a result of stacking the textbooks? Describe how mass might affect the amount of force needed to cause motion down a ramp.

In the space provided, **sketch** a graph showing your data. What relationship did you see between the mass of the objects and the change in their motion?

Activity 6
Analyze

Quick Code
ca8033s

Mass and Force

Read the following text. **Identify** cause-and-effect relationships in the text. **Circle** the cause portion of the statements and **underline** the effect relationships.

EXPLORE

Mass and Force

We recognize that forces are acting on objects that are not in **motion**. As a rocket sits on the launchpad at rest, **gravity** is applying a downward **force** on the rocket. Additionally, the launchpad is pushing up on the rocket to balance the force of gravity. The rocket may also be pushing against the tower on the launchpad, which is applying a force to hold up the rocket at the correct launch angle for the mission.

If NASA engineers want the rocket to travel straight up into the air, where should they apply the force? How much force should they apply? The materials used on a rocket are selected because they can perform under strenuous conditions throughout the rocket's mission. It is important that engineers select the appropriate amount of force to push the rocket into low Earth **orbit**. Too much force can cause parts of the rocket to fail, as well as provide too heavy of a load to lift the rocket off of the ground.

Apollo Rocket

Engineers consider the **mass** of the rocket when determining the needed force to move the rocket from the launchpad. What do you think is the relationship between the mass of an object and the force needed to move the object?

To provide the necessary force to lift a rocket off the launchpad, engineers use either solid or liquid fuel. The rocket fuel has chemical **potential energy** based on the chemical bonds within the propellant. This chemical potential energy is released when the propellant is burned. The reaction, which results in combustion, creates the force necessary to overcome the force of gravity and launch the rocket off the launchpad. The greater the mass, the more force is needed to put the rocket into motion.

The Saturn V rocket, considered a heavy lift vehicle, weighed 2.8 million kilograms at launch, the **weight** of about 400 elephants. Fuel onboard provided 34.5 million Newtons of force to launch the Saturn V off of the launchpad. Not all the fuel onboard a rocket is used to launch the vehicle. The rocket will conserve some of the potential energy in the fuel to use later in the mission to change the direction and **speed** of the rocket in orbit.

Activity 7

Evaluate

Quick Code
ca8034s

Rocket Mass and Force

The space shuttle is an example of a rocket with a variable payload. If the same amount of fuel is used to launch the space shuttle carrying different payloads, how do you predict the speed at launch will vary? From the list provided, **rank** the payload masses from greatest speed to slowest speed at launch.

1.04 million kg	2.44 million kg	2.84 million kg
2.004 million kg	2.04 million kg	

Speed	Payload Mass
Greatest Speed	
Slowest Speed	

CCC **Energy and Matter**

Use Newton's second law, $f = ma$, to explain why engineers must take into account the total mass of a rocket in determining how much fuel they need to launch the rocket.

EXPLORE

Activity 8

Observe

Rockets and Newton's Third Law

Quick Code
ca8035s

As you watch this video, **look** for examples of causes and effects of specific events.

Rockets and Newton's Third Law

Use the graphic organizer to record examples of cause-and-effect relationships that you noted in the video.

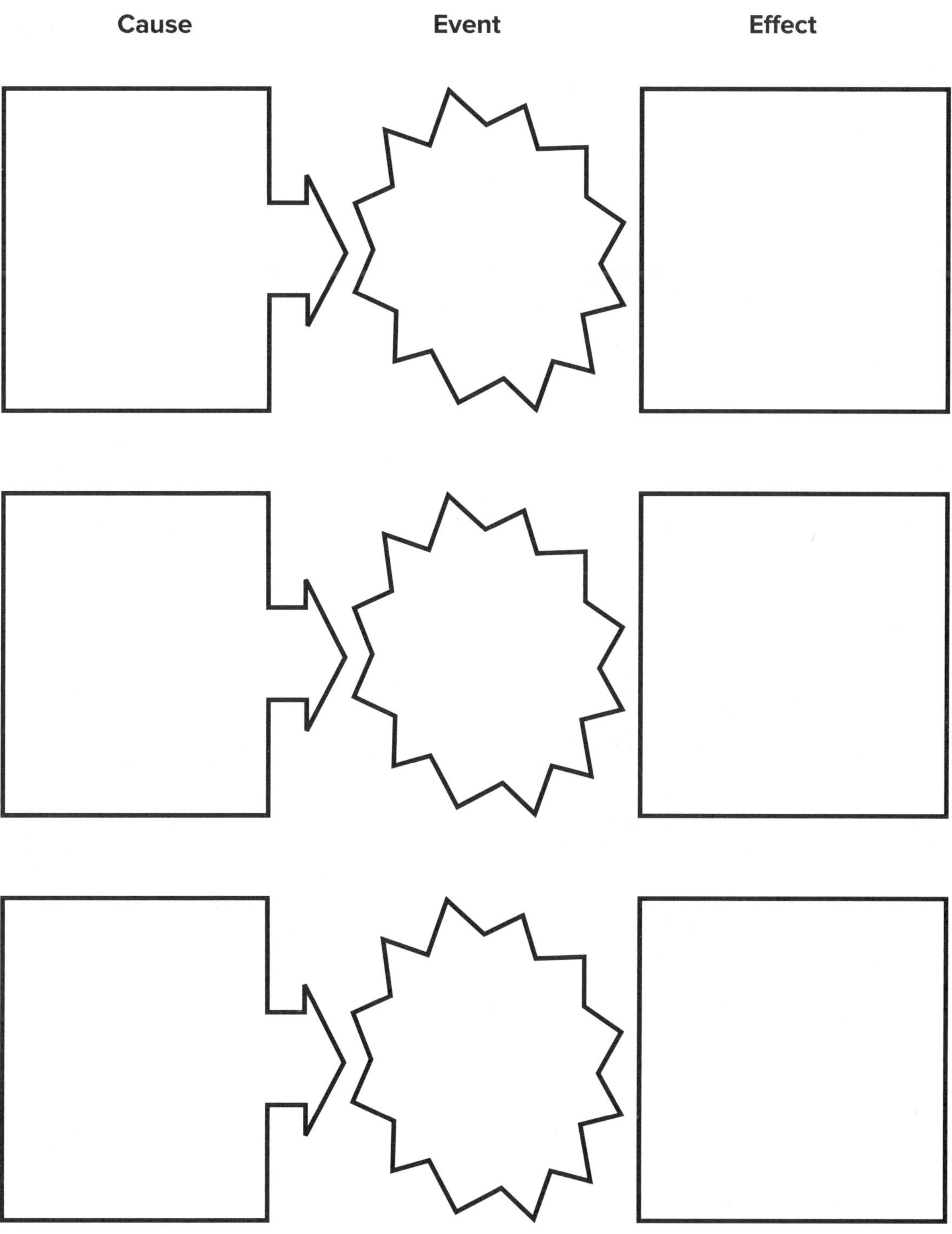

EXPLORE

Activity 9

Evaluate

Quick Code
ca8036s

Thrust

Review the image. Using oars to propel a boat across the water is an example of Newton's third law of motion.

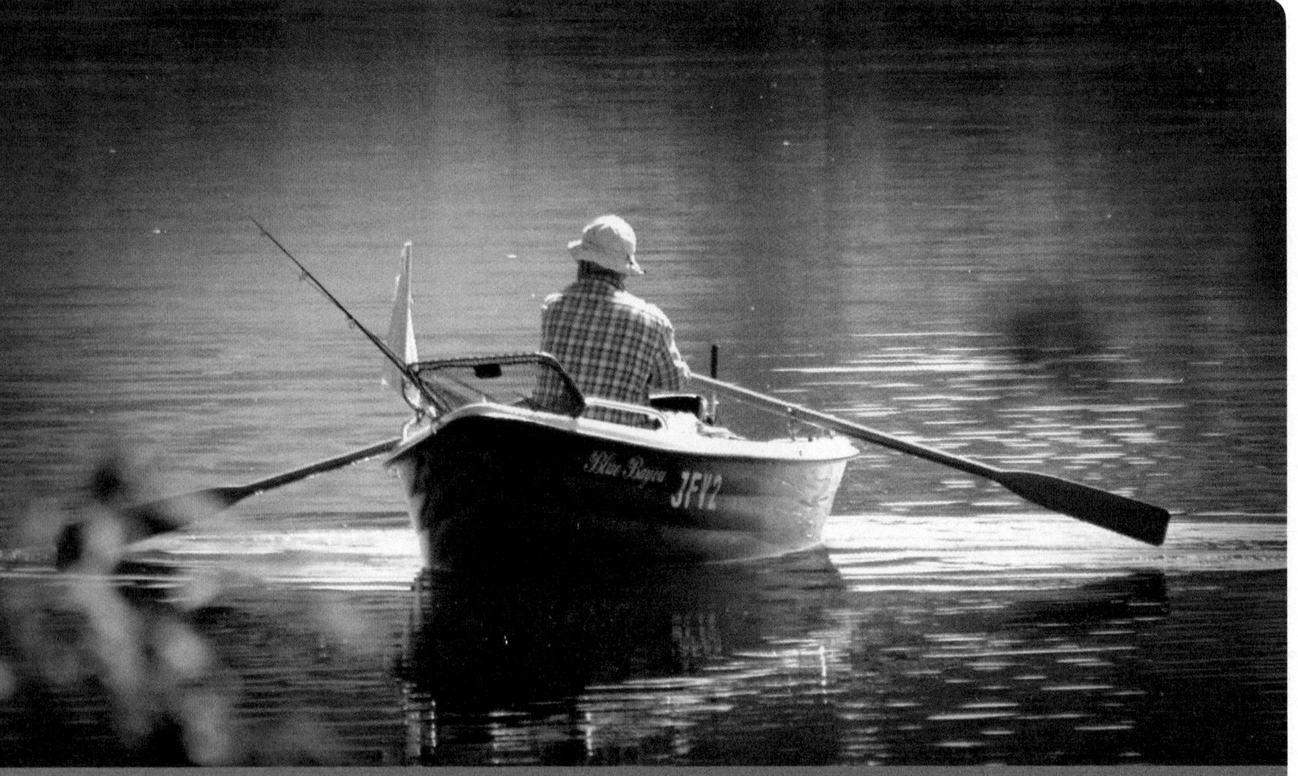

Thrust

Identify the action and reaction force in the image.

___

___

___

Provide a written explanation that describes the action-reaction relationship of a person rowing a rowboat.

Generate testable questions that could be used to design an investigation to support Newton's third law.

EXPLORE

How Do We Measure the Velocity and Acceleration of a Rocket?

Activity 10

Analyze

Quick Code
ca8037s

Accelerating into Orbit

Read the following text. **Use** the equation for acceleration to calculate the acceleration of the Saturn V rocket for each time interval represented in the data table. **Add** your five calculations to the Acceleration column.

Accelerating into Orbit

As the rocket begins its ascent, it accelerates to reach the appropriate speed for the given mission. **Acceleration** is the rate at which an object changes velocity. As the velocity of the object increases, so does the kinetic energy of the object. This makes sense, as we know that the **potential energy** of the rocket fuel is being converted to kinetic energy.

A very high acceleration could cause an object to speed up very quickly, but does not necessarily mean that the object will be traveling very fast. For example, a person jogging might jog from rest to 5 meters per second in a time of 5 seconds. A runner could sprint from rest to 5 meters per second in 1 second. In this case, the jogger has an acceleration of 1 meter

SEP **Analyzing and Interpreting Data**

per second squared, and the sprinter has an acceleration of 5 meter per second squared. The sprinter sped up much faster; however, both runners end up running at exactly the same final speed.

If an object starts with an initial velocity of v_i and a final velocity of v_f, and it changes velocity over a time t:

$$a = \frac{v_f - v_i}{t}$$

So, if a runner is jogging with a velocity of 2 meters per second north and then accelerates to 6 meters per second north in a time of 2 seconds, her acceleration would be:

$$a = \frac{(6 \text{ m/s} - 2 \text{ m/s})}{2\text{s}} = \frac{4 \text{ m/s}}{2\text{s}} = 2 \text{ m/s}^2 \text{ north}$$

The units of acceleration are given in length per time squared. The common units of acceleration are "meters per second squared," or m/s^2. Like velocity, acceleration also has a direction associated with it.

Measurement tools are onboard rockets for engineers to measure the change in altitude and speed of the rocket during its mission. Instrumentation on the Saturn V rocket, launched in 1969, recorded the altitude and speed data of the rocket after launch.

EXPLORE

Can you calculate the acceleration, at various intervals, for the Saturn V?

Saturn V Rocket Launch Speed and Height

Time (sec)	Altitude (m)	Speed (m/s)	Acceleration (m/s^2)
0	0	0	
5	32	12	
10	126	25	
15	269	39	
20	510	56	

[Source: NASA]

How Is Energy Transferred When Launching a Rocket?

Activity 11

Analyze

Kinetic Energy Data

Quick Code
ca8038s

Read the following text, and then **answer** the questions that follow.

EXPLORE

Kinetic Energy Data

Any object in motion has kinetic energy. The larger the object, the more kinetic energy it has. Additionally, when an object travels faster, it also has more kinetic energy. Let's look at some examples of objects in motion.

In a softball game, the pitcher stands on the mound, which is 13 meters from home plate. When the ball is in the pitcher's hand and not moving, it has zero kinetic energy because it is not in motion. However, when she throws the ball, it has kinetic energy. Specifically, the chemical potential energy in her body changes into the mechanical energy of her arm moving, which then turns into the kinetic energy of the ball. Suppose that the softball arrives at home plate in 0.438 seconds. Can you determine the speed with which the

SEP Analyzing and Interpreting Data

softball travels? If you are given that the mass is 187 grams, can you determine the kinetic energy of the ball after it is thrown?

At the start of a horse race, all the horses are lined up in a gate. The horses and their jockeys wait until a starter pistol is fired. The sound lets them all know to start the race. The gates open, and the horses rush out. As the horses increase in speed, they gain kinetic energy. When they remain at the same speed, they maintain the same amount of kinetic energy. When they stop at the end of the race, they lose their kinetic energy. If a horse with a mass of 544 kilograms completes a 2.4-kilometer racetrack in 3 minutes, what is its speed and kinetic energy?

Human-made satellites orbit Earth to provide communication, data, and entertainment. To ensure that they stay in the same position above Earth, they need to stay in a geosynchronous orbit. This orbit allows the satellite to keep up with the rotation of Earth.

Object	Distance	Time	Speed	Mass
Softball	13 m	0.438 s		187 g
Horse	2.4 km	3 min		544 kg
Satellite	265,000 km	24 hr		800 kg

Answer the following questions.

Of the three objects considered, which has the greatest kinetic energy? How do you know?

____

When does the horse gain kinetic energy?

____

____

Complete the chart to find the speed and kinetic energy for each object. **Write** your answers in the appropriate columns.

Object	Distance	Time	Speed	Mass	Kinetic Energy
Softball	13 m	0.438 s		187 g	
Horse	2.4 km	3 min		544 kg	
Satellite	265,000 km	24 hr		800 kg	

Using the chart, **rank** the objects from most to least amount of kinetic energy.

____

EXPLORE

Activity 12

Observe

Quick Code ca8039s

Moving On

Go online to explore how energy conditions change as objects move. In this Interactive, you will choose balls of different masses and release them at different heights to observe the changing energy conditions as they bounce.

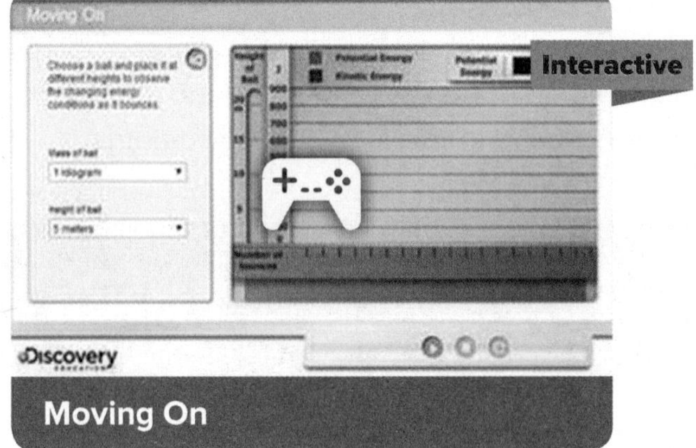

Moving On

In the Interactive online, **choose** the mass of a ball and **place** it at different heights to observe the changing energy conditions as it bounces. **Count** the bounces and **record** them in the chart as potential energy in Joules (J).

Mass of Ball	Height of Ball	Potential Energy (J)
1 kg	5 m	
1 kg	10 m	
1 kg	20 m	
2 kg	5 m	
2 kg	10 m	
2 kg	20 m	
4 kg	5 m	
4 kg	10 m	
4 kg	20 m	

EXPLORE

Answer the following questions.

Define kinetic energy.

____

What did you observe about each subsequent bounce for every bounce from every height?

____

What was the relationship of potential energy to kinetic energy? Why?

____

____

____

Activity 13

Investigate

Quick Code
ca8040s

Hands-On Investigation: Kinetic Energy, Speed, and Mass

In this activity, you will measure and plot the relationship between kinetic energy and speed and the relationship between mass and speed for a handful of objects.

Predict

How will speed change when objects of differing mass move with the same kinetic energy?

SEP Planning and Carrying Out Investigations

SEP Analyzing and Interpreting Data

CCC Patterns

What materials do you need? (per group)

- Paper
- Graph paper
- Pencils
- Balance, triple beam
- Stopwatch
- Metersticks
- Masking tape
- Marbles, 1 in.
- Tennis balls
- Whiffle balls
- Billiard balls

EXPLORE

Procedure

Part 1: Varying Speed to Observe Changes in Kinetic Energy

Roll an object on a flat surface to measure the following:

- The speed of the rolled object

  ____

- The mass of the object

  ____

- The distance the rolled object traveled

  ____

  ____

  ____

- The time it takes the rolled object to roll the distance it traveled

  ____

Use the same object, but change the speeds at which it moves. Run at least five trials for each mass traveling at different speeds. What did you notice?

____

____

Calculate the speed of the object for each trial and then the kinetic energy for each trial. List the kinetic energy results. What do you notice?

____

____

Use the space provided or a piece of graph paper to plot speed versus kinetic energy and analyze the relationship between these variables.

Part 2: Varying Mass to Observe Changes in Speed

Roll an object down a ramp so that it strikes another object at the bottom of the ramp. Measure the speed of the second object as it moves along the floor or table. For each test, vary the mass of the second object, but keep the mass of the first object constant.

For each test, measure the following:

- The masses of each second object you used at the base of the ramp

- The distance that the second object travels after the rolled object collides with it

- The time it takes for the second object to roll the distance measured

Calculate the speed of the second object for each trial and then the kinetic energy for each trial. Use your calculations to make a statement about the kinetic energy throughout the experiments.

Use the space provided or a piece of graph paper to plot mass versus speed and analyze the relationship between these variables.

Reflect

Review your hypothesis. Did the results of the investigation provide evidence that supports your hypothesis? Or, did it provide evidence against your hypothesis? Describe how you know.

Based on your results, how are speed and kinetic energy related to each other? Explain your answer.

Based on your results, how are mass and speed related to each other? Explain your answer.

EXPLORE

Activity 14
Analyze

Quick Code
ca8041s

Energy in Systems

Read the following text. Then, **create** a model representing the energy flow during the launch of a rocket and the rocket's return to Earth. **Construct** your energy flow diagram on a separate sheet of paper.

Energy in Systems

To analyze the transfer of energy in a system, you need to consider the energy source in the system and what object is receiving the energy put into the system. Consider someone lifting a **weight** up off the ground. In this example, the person lifting the weight is doing work. The person is the energy source of the system. The energy is transferred to the weight, which becomes the receiver of the energy. The work of the person is

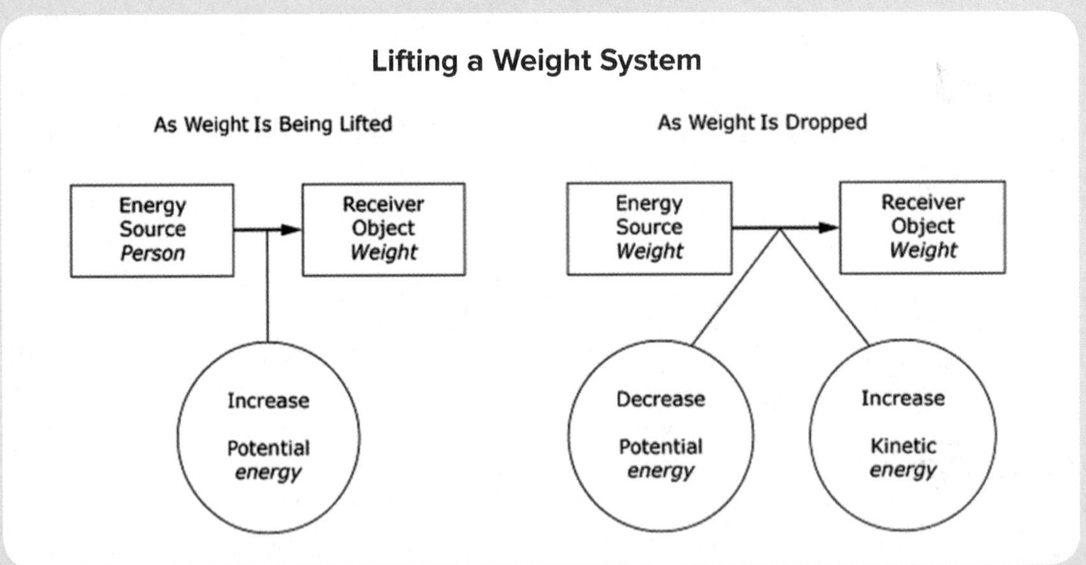

SEP Developing and Using Models

CCC Energy and Matter

transferred to gravitational potential energy in the weight. Once the person drops the weight, the gravitational potential energy added to the system, plus the chemical potential energy of the ball, in its resting state, are converted to kinetic energy.

As a rocket lifts off, it gains gravitational potential energy. Gravitational potential energy is the energy stored in an object that has been lifted up against the **force** of **gravity**. Gravitational potential energy is proportional to distance from the ground. Similarly, a rocket with more mass will also have more gravitational potential energy. This is because gravitational potential energy is also proportional to mass. It takes a lot of work to lift a massive object up against gravity, so you store more potential energy in a heavy object than you do in a lighter object.

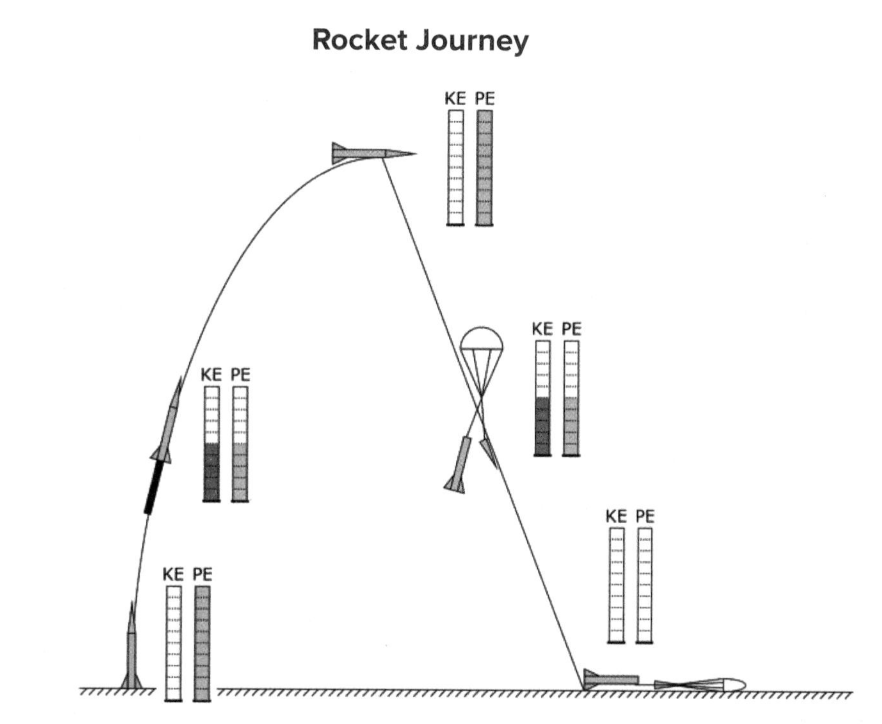

EXPLORE

Activity 15

Investigate

Quick Code
ca8042s

Hands-On Investigation: Potential Energy of Marbles

In this activity, you and your group will design a ramp to investigate how height affects the potential energy of an object. Your group will run multiple trials of each condition tested. You will apply scientific inquiry methods through repeated trials to construct a data table.

Predict

How will height change the potential energy of an object? How will the distance an object moves be related to its original potential energy?

SEP Planning and Carrying Out Investigations

What materials do you need? (per group)

- Cardboard paper towel tube
- Metersticks
- Metric ruler
- Masking tape
- Books with different thicknesses
- Collision ball, 16 mm
- Collision ball, 25 mm
- Collision ball, 38 mm

EXPLORE

Procedure

Construct ramps of various heights to test your hypotheses. Test all three marbles at different heights. Record your findings in a data table like the one shown here.

	Marble 1			Marble 2			Marble 3		
	Test 1	Test 2	Test 3	Test 1	Test 2	Test 3	Test 1	Test 2	Test 3
Height #1 ______ **cm**									
Height #2 ______ **cm**									
Height #3 ______ **cm**									
Variable with Ramp									
Variable with Floor									
Control Test with No Ramp									

Reflect

What factors might affect your results, especially when comparing your results with those of other groups?

How can you use height to change the potential energy of an object?

How will the distance an object moves be related to its original potential energy?

EXPLORE

Activity 16

Evaluate

Conservation of Energy

Quick Code
ca8043s

When a rubber ball is thrown against a wall, energy is transferred and transformed.

In the space provided, **construct** a simple energy diagram of a ball thrown against a wall.

SEP Engaging in Argument from Evidence

Select the statement from the list that does NOT support the law of conservation of energy.

- ◯ Before the ball is thrown, it has the highest potential energy due to the position of the thrower's arm.
- ◯ When the ball is released, the thrower's arm transfers its energy to the ball.
- ◯ After it is thrown, all of the ball's potential energy becomes kinetic energy.
- ◯ When the ball hits the wall, it compresses, transforming its kinetic energy to potential energy.
- ◯ The ball returns to its original shape and propels from the wall, transforming its potential energy to kinetic energy.

EXPLORE

In the space provided, **diagram** a bouncing ball's kinetic and potential energies as shown (1) when the ball is released and (2) when it hits the ground.

EXPLORE

Activity 17

Record Evidence

Quick Code
ca8044s

Rockets

As you worked through this lesson, you investigated and gathered evidence about energy for launch. Now, take another look at the video Rockets, which you first saw in Engage.

How has your understanding of Rockets changed?

Read the Can You Explain? question from the beginning of this lesson.

Can You Explain?

How do mass and energy affect the acceleration of a rocket?

SEP **Constructing Explanations and Designing Solutions**

Plan a scientific explanation to answer the Can You Explain? or a question of your own. Recall that a scientific explanation contains three elements: a scientific claim, evidence to support the claim, and reasoning that connects the evidence to the claim. Use this planning chart to develop your scientific explanation:

Scientific Explanation Planning Chart
What is my claim?
What data from my investigations can I use to support my claim?

EXPLAIN

What reliable evidence from the text and/or videos can I use as evidence?

Which scientific ideas, principles, and/or laws apply to my explanation?

Now, **use** the information in your planning chart to **write** your scientific explanation.

Scientific Explanation (Explanation = Claim + Evidence + Logical Reasoning)	
Directions: Create a scientific explanation for the question. This combines the claim that was made, the evidence that was collected, and a justification for why the evidence supports the claim (logical reasoning). The explanation should contain clear thoughts and accurate scientific vocabulary.	Key Components: • Uses precise and accurate language • Uses scientific vocabulary • Provides clear, logical thoughts • Uses evidence and reasoning to support the claim

EXPLAIN

STEM in Action

Activity 18

Analyze

Quick Code
ca8045s

Rocket Science Curiosity

Read the following text and **view** the two videos. Then, **complete** the activities that follow.

Rocket Science Curiosity

When a task isn't very hard to do, a person might say, "It's not rocket science." This is a common expression that suggests that, while other things may be very simple, rocket science is a very difficult task. However, the basic physics of a rocket are actually quite simple! A rocket moves according to Newton's third law of **motion**. When jet fuel shoots from the back of a rocket, it applies an equal and opposite **force** back on the rocket. This force propels the rocket forward.

Video

The Curiosity Landing: Seven Minutes of Terror

SEP Using Mathematics and Computational Thinking

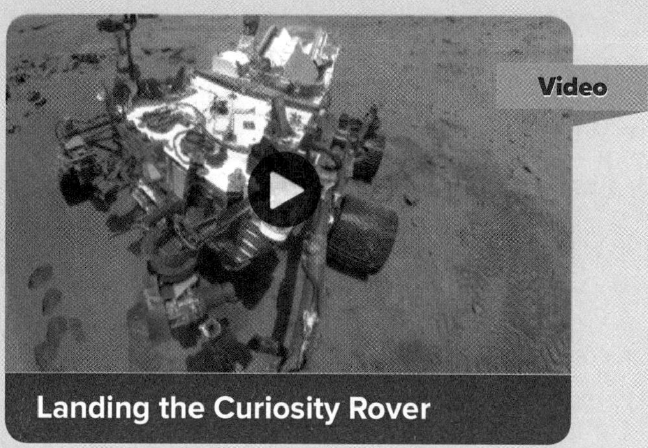

Landing the Curiosity Rover

Newton's first and second laws of motion also apply to the motion of the rocket as it moves through space. For example, once the rocket has escaped Earth's gravitational pull, it will continue on a straight path until it encounters another external force. This is Newton's first law. Similarly, if a rocket is going to land, it must decelerate according to Newton's second law in order to come to a stop.

Engineers must apply Newton's laws when considering space travel. Let's explore the work of Dr. Anita Sengupta, an amazing aerospace engineer at NASA who helped land the Curiosity rover on Mars

When the Curiosity rover was sent to land on Mars, Sengupta was the lead engineer in charge of making sure the rover landed safely. Basically, she was in charge of designing the parachute to slow the rover down. This was challenging because the rover is 533 kilograms (almost 2,000 pounds) and approximately the size of a regular Jeep. Another challenge was that the atmosphere of Mars is very thin. This means that the atmosphere would not help slow the rover.

Though there were many complex variables that Sengupta had to consider, the basic physics is explained by Newton's second law. The rover had a **mass** of 533 kilograms. It had to decelerate from approximately 5,300 meters per second to 0 meters per second at the surface of Mars in 7 minutes. Using Newton's second law, the force required to do this can be calculated. Sengupta used a combination of a heat shield, parachute, and additional rockets to slow the rover. When asked how she approached the task, she said,

"You approach it methodically. You think about all the different aspects of the parachute descent, all the things that could go wrong, all the different ways to address those problems, and then you design a test program to address all of those aspects."

The Curiosity rover ended up landing successfully on Mars. Sengupta made rocket science look easy!

It's not enough for scientists to just know facts. When designing solutions to problems, scientists must rely on their persistence, prevision, reasoning, logic, imagination, and creativity. In the chart, **identify** one example from the text and videos that links back to each of the human qualities listed.

	Definition	Example from the Text and/or Video
Persistence		
Precision		
Reasoning		

ELABORATE

	Definition	Example from the Text and/or Video
Logic		
Imagination		
Creativity		

Calculating Average Force

We can calculate the average acceleration of the Curiosity rover during its landing on Mars using the initial velocity, v_i, the final velocity, v_f, and the time it took to stop:

$$a = \frac{v_f - v_i}{t}$$

According to Newton's second law, the average force required to slow the Curiosity rover to a stop, F, is equal to the mass of the rover, m, multiplied by its average acceleration, a:

$$F = ma$$

Use these equations to calculate the average force required to stop the Curiosity rover if the initial velocity is 5,300 meters per second, the final velocity is 0 meters per second, the time required to stop is 7 minutes, and the mass of the rover is 533 kilograms. (Be sure to convert the time, 7 minutes, to seconds!)

ELABORATE

Considering Actual Force

Based on the video segment The Curiosity Landing: Seven Minutes of Terror, do you think your calculation in the previous item accurately describes the force that the rover would experience for the entirety of its landing? **Explain** your reasoning. If not, do you think the rover would experience stronger or weaker forces during its descent?

ELABORATE

Activity 19

Concept Review

Review: Energy for Launch

Quick Code
ca8046s

Now that you have completed the objectives for this concept, **review** the core ideas you have learned. Record some of the core ideas in the space provided.

Core Ideas

Talk with a Group

Now, think about the asteroid impact crater video you saw in Get Started. Discuss how what you've learned about energy for launch can help you understand an asteroid colliding with Earth.

EVALUATE

CONCEPT

1.3

Colliding Objects

Student Objectives

By the end of this lesson:

- [ ] I can develop small-scale and planetary-scale models that describe and predict how systems interact during collisions as they gain, lose, and transfer energy.
- [ ] I can design and carry out investigations to collect and analyze data that describe the linear relationships among force, mass, and acceleration in collisions and to predict the effect of change in one variable on other variables.
- [ ] I can argue from evidence that every action has an equal and opposite reaction.
- [ ] I can design, evaluate, and defend solutions to mitigate safety risks in collision systems.
- [ ] I can carry out investigations to describe patterns in different types of collisions.

Key Vocabulary

acceleration, asteroid, atmosphere, comet, crater, force, gravity, kinetic energy, mass, meteor, planet, velocity

Quick Code
ca8048s

Activity 1

Can You Explain?

How much energy would an asteroid impact transfer to Earth's surface?

Quick Code
ca8049s

Activity 2

Ask Questions

Quick Code
ca8050s

Meteorites Hitting Earth

Space objects, such as meteors, enter our **atmosphere** and fall toward Earth. How frequently does this happen? Are certain areas of Earth in more danger than other areas? If a large enough **meteor** hits Earth, could it shake Earth off of its axis?

Watch the following video.

Video

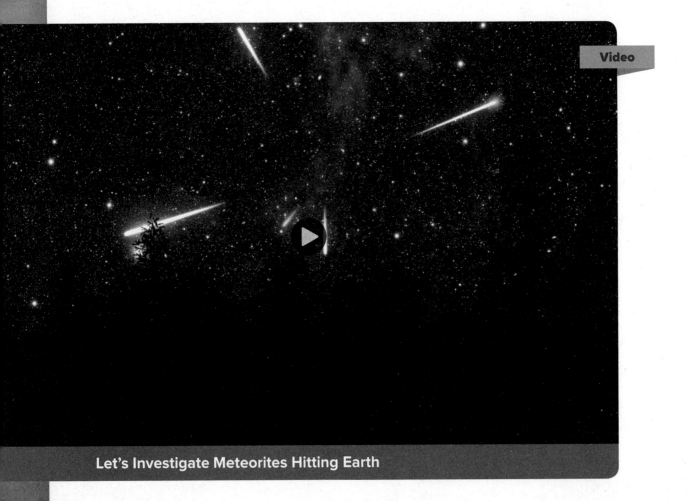

Let's Investigate Meteorites Hitting Earth

Near-Earth Objects

Work with a partner. One of you will spin a coin on its end to represent Earth spinning around its axis. The other person will try to knock the coin off of its axis.

Then, **read** this claim.

> Near-Earth objects (NEOs) are large enough to knock Earth off of its axis.

What questions would you need to answer before you could support or refute this claim?

ENGAGE

Activity 3

Interpret Data

Small Asteroids

Quick Code ca8051s

Read the text, then **answer** the questions that follow.

NASA scientists and engineers at the Planetary Defense Coordination Office (PDCO) are tasked with protecting Earth from near-Earth objects (NEOs), which could reach Earth's surface. An NEO means that an **asteroid** or **comet**'s orbit is within approximately 30 million miles of Earth's orbit. The PDCO uses technology to detect potentially hazardous objects (PHOs), such as asteroids, comets, and meteorites. An NEO is considered a PHO if it is larger than 140 meters across. If a potential impact is identified, the PDCO is responsible for communicating the information to U.S. government officials, media, and the public.

Small Asteroids

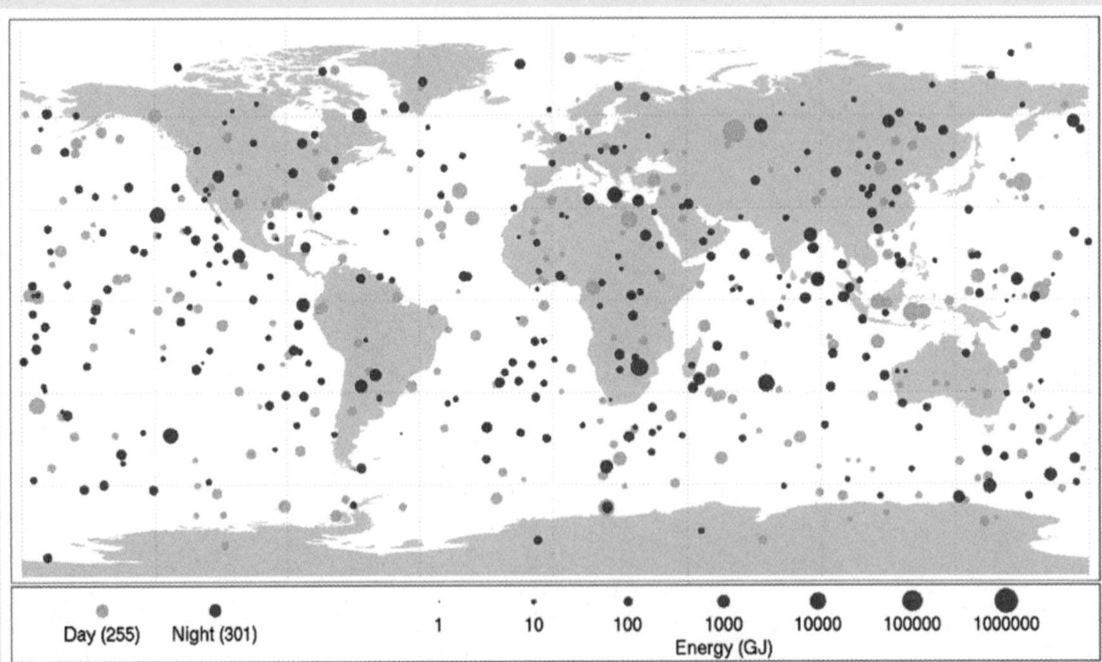

SEP Engaging in Argument from Evidence

What two claims can you make about patterns in the data about small asteroids?

Which data points support your claims?

ENGAGE

Activity 4

Analyze

Quick Code
ca8052s

Asteroid Impact

Read the text and **watch** the video about asteroid impact. Then, **answer** the following question.

What evidence is there of energy conversion in the simulation of an asteroid impact?

Asteroid Impact

Although the exact date is debated by scientists, approximately 65.5 million years ago, an asteroid did enter the atmosphere and crash into Earth's surface. The asteroid formed a **crater** 180 kilometers in diameter in Chicxulub, Mexico. It has been calculated that the asteroid took only 1.5 seconds to reach Earth's surface after entering the atmosphere. This means that the asteroid was traveling at a speed of 66.7 kilometers per second. If the PDCO would have been able to detect the NEO, it would have been nearly impossible to warn anyone of the impact.

Simulation of Asteroid Impact

ENGAGE

Activity 5

Evaluate

Quick Code
ca8053s

What Do You Already Know About Colliding Objects?

Action and Reaction

In a vehicle collision, pairs of forces occur while the car is on the road and at the moment of impact. **Review** the diagrams and **circle** the one that shows the correct pair of forces for the situation.

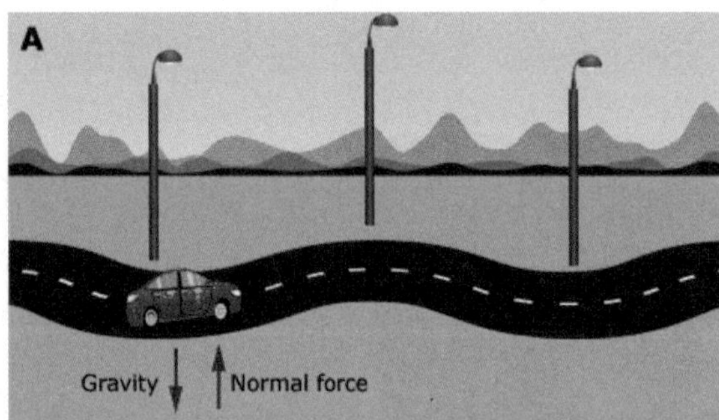

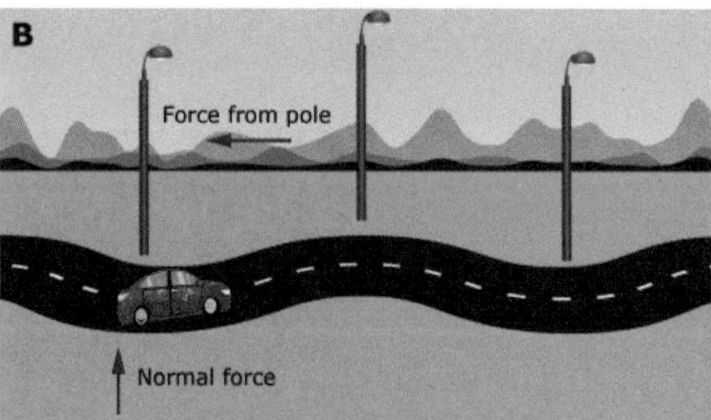

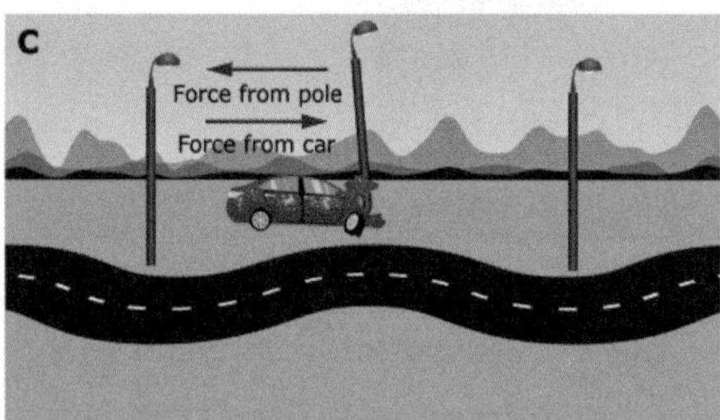

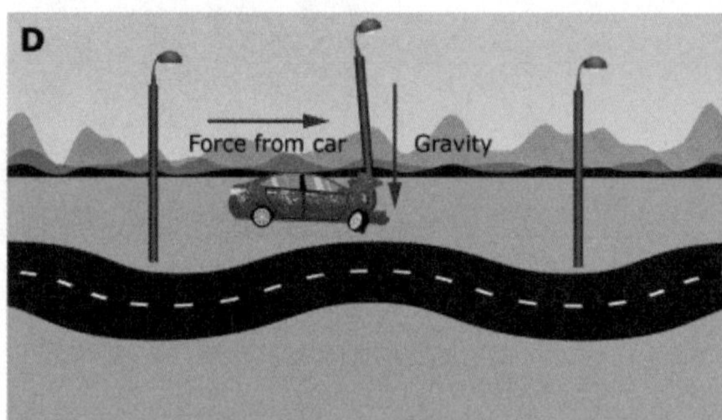

ENGAGE

Collisions in Bowling

A bowling ball is thrown and strikes the pins, knocking them down. As this happens, how is energy transferred in the bowling ball and pin system? **Draw** an arrow between the bowling ball and pins to show the correct direction for how kinetic energy is transferred.

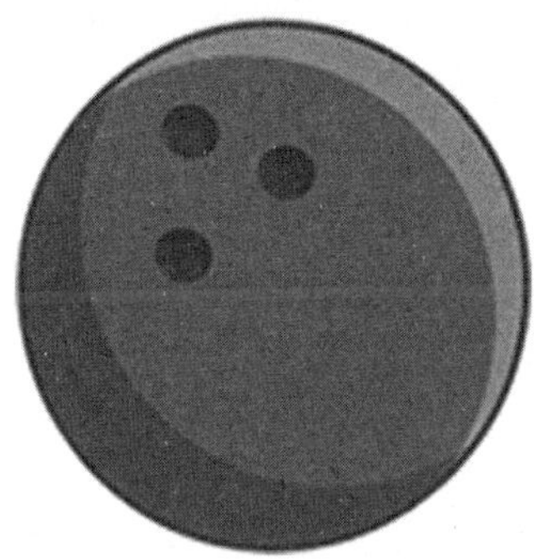

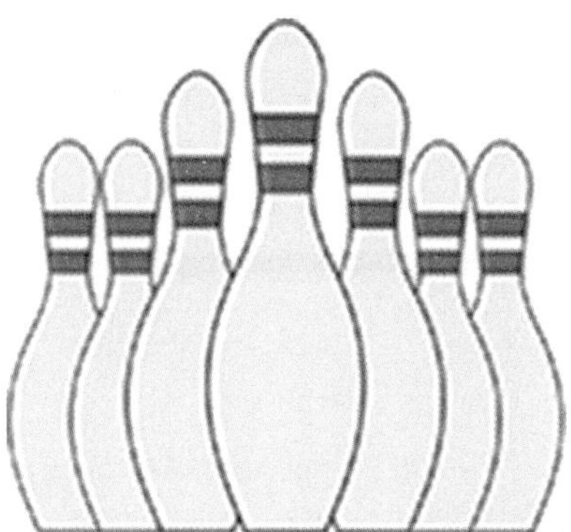

Share your response with another student and **discuss** your responses.

Moving Along

An investigation was conducted to find the effect of mass on force. Four balls of different masses were used. Balls were released from six different distances measured along a ramp placed at a 15° angle from the horizontal plane of the floor.

Ball Type	Mass (g)
Plastic	10.6
Golf	112.98
Steel	249.98
Rubber	61.75

A plastic cup was placed at the end of the ramp. After each roll, the distance the cup moved was measured in centimeters.

Ramp

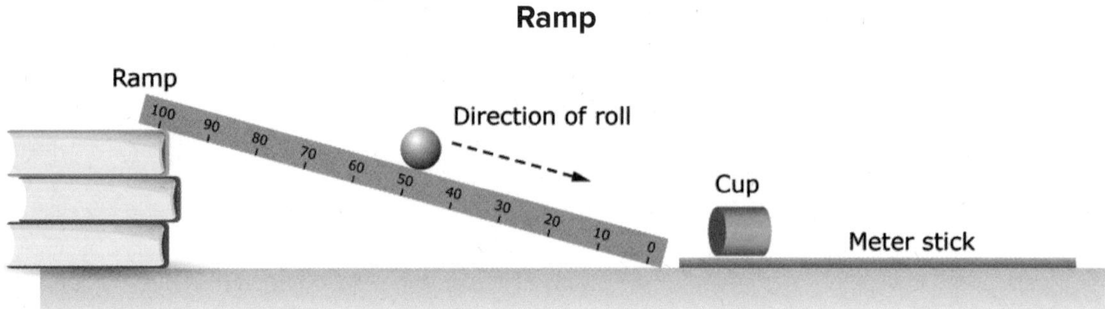

How is the mass of each ball related to its force on the cup? **Review** the graph of the data from the investigation and **complete** the graph's legend by adding the type of ball.

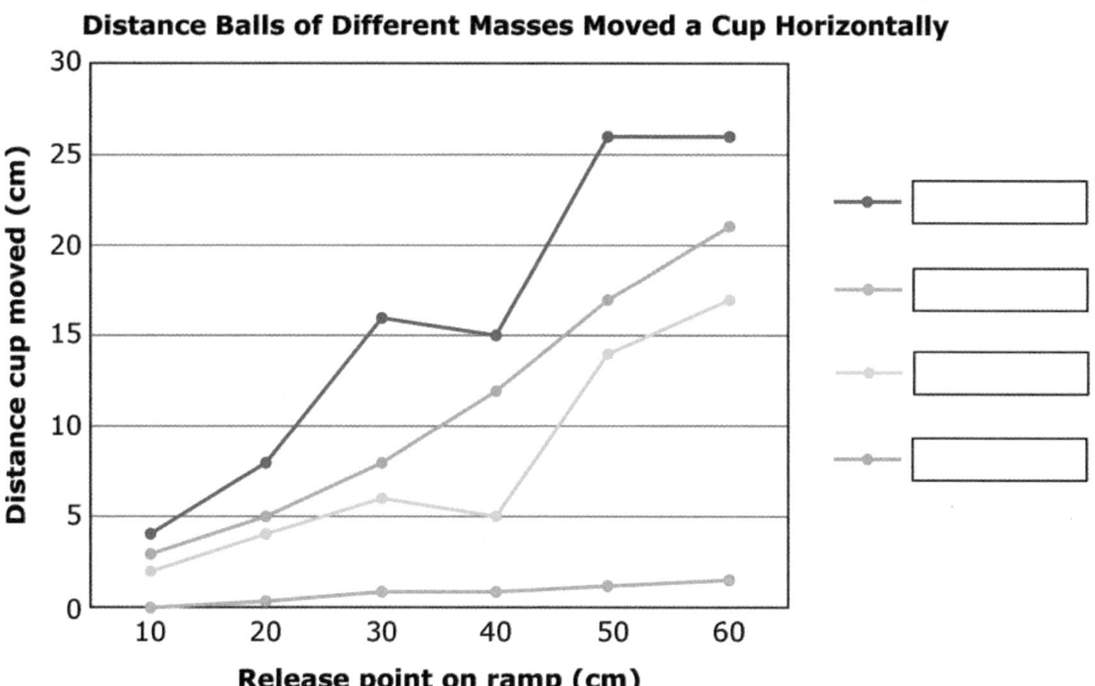

How Do Changes in Force and Mass Affect Collisions?

Activity 6

Investigate

Quick Code
ca8054s

Hands-On Investigation: Applying Newton's Third Law to Collisions

In this investigation, you will explore how the mass of an object and forces acting on an object affect the object's motion.

Predict

How will an increase in the mass of an object affect its motion?

SEP Planning and Carrying out Investigations

SEP Engaging in Argument from Evidence

SEP Using Mathematics and Computational Thinking

What materials do you need? (per group)

- Cardboard paper towel tube
- Metersticks
- Metric ruler
- Masking tape
- Safety goggles (per student)
- Collision ball, 16 mm
- Collision ball, 19 mm
- Collision ball, 25 mm
- Collision ball, 38 mm

Procedure

1. Use the materials to design an investigation to provide evidence that mass affects the applied forces on objects in a collision. Your investigation should include identification of independent and dependent variables and controls, tools for measurement, and data-collection methods.

2. Describe your investigation. Include drawings if necessary.

Now, complete your investigation. Create and complete a table like the one shown, a graph, or other means of recording the data you gather during your investigation.

Effect of Changing Mass on an Object's Motion

Marble Placed on Track	Trial	Ramp Height (cm)	Ramp Height (cm)
#1 (smallest)	1	15 cm	
#1 (medium)	2	15 cm	
#1 (largest)	3	15 cm	
			Average:
#2 (smallest)	1	15 cm	
#2 (medium)	2	15 cm	
#2 (largest)	3	15 cm	
			Average:
#3 (smallest)	1	15 cm	
#3 (medium)	2	15 cm	
#3 (largest)	3	15 cm	
			Average:

Now, design an investigation to explore the effect of changing the applied force on the change of motion of a given object. Describe your investigation, including drawings if needed.

EXPLORE

Complete your second investigation. Create and complete a table like the one shown, a graph, or other means of recording the data you gather in your investigation.

Effect of Changing Applied Force on an Object's Motion

Ramp Height (cm)	Trial	Marble Placed on Track	Distance Traveled by Marble 2
10 cm	1	#1 (smallest)	
10 cm	2	#1 (smallest)	
10 cm	3	#1 (smallest)	
			Average:
20 cm	1	#1 (smallest)	
20 cm	2	#1 (smallest)	
20 cm	3	#1 (smallest)	
			Average:
25 cm	1	#1 (smallest)	
25 cm	2	#1 (smallest)	
25 cm	3	#1 (smallest)	
			Average:

Reflect

What evidence did your investigation provide? What claim does your evidence support?

EXPLORE

Activity 7

Analyze

Quick Code
ca8055s

Equal and Opposite Forces

Read the text, Then, **complete** the activity that follows.

Equal and Opposite Forces

Newton's third law states that for every action, there is an equal and opposite reaction. To state this idea another way, forces come in pairs; when one object applies a **force** to a second object, the second object applies an equal force to the first object.

In systems where forces are not balanced and objects are in motion, do we observe equal and opposite forces when objects collide? For example, if you throw a bowling ball, with a **mass** of 5 kilograms, to knock down a bowling pin, with a mass of 1.5 kilograms, and then you try to throw a small rubber ball, with a mass of 1 kilograms, to knock down the pin, will the pin experience the same force? In which instance will you observe the pin moving?

Newton's second law quantifies force as $F = ma$. In this equation, F is the force being applied to an object, m is the mass of the object, and a is the resulting rate of **acceleration**.

CCC **Systems and System Models**

For each object in the collision, we can calculate the force, if we know:

- the mass of the object and
- the acceleration of the object

In the example, the bowling ball is more massive than the small rubber ball. Therefore, the force applied to the pin is greater in the bowling ball collision. This larger force is applied to the pin, causing the pin to accelerate to the back of the bowling alley. The pin applies a force on the bowling ball, which causes the bowling ball to decrease its acceleration.

While some asteroids are found near the inner and outer planets, most form a large belt between Mars and Jupiter. These asteroids are often located hundreds of thousands of miles away from each other. Asteroids rotate or tumble, often erratically, and revolve around the sun in elliptical orbits. They tend to have an irregular shape and are often dotted with craters made from collisions with other nonplanetary objects. Some asteroids are nearly spherical in shape.

About 150 asteroids have one or two smaller bodies orbiting them like moons. While most asteroids remain in the asteroid belt, occasionally the **gravity** of Jupiter, Mars, or a collision with another nonplanetary object may send an asteroid moving out of the belt. Some of these stray asteroids have collided with other planets, including Earth. In fact, some scientists believe that such a collision was the source of the mass dinosaur extinction 65 million years ago.

Scientists believe that when an asteroid the size of Chicxulub hit Earth, it broke into millions of pieces. However, Earth's response to the impact resulted in a crater, which compacted and ejected Earth's materials; however, Earth was not knocked off its orbit. The ejected Earth materials have been recorded to cover nearly 48,000 cubic miles from the site of impact. Does this mean that Earth experienced less force than the asteroid?

Now, **compare** any system mentioned in the text, such as the bowling ball and rubber ball or the asteroid and Earth, with the system you tested in the activity Applying Newton's Third Law to Collisions. **Use** the Venn diagram to display your comparisons.

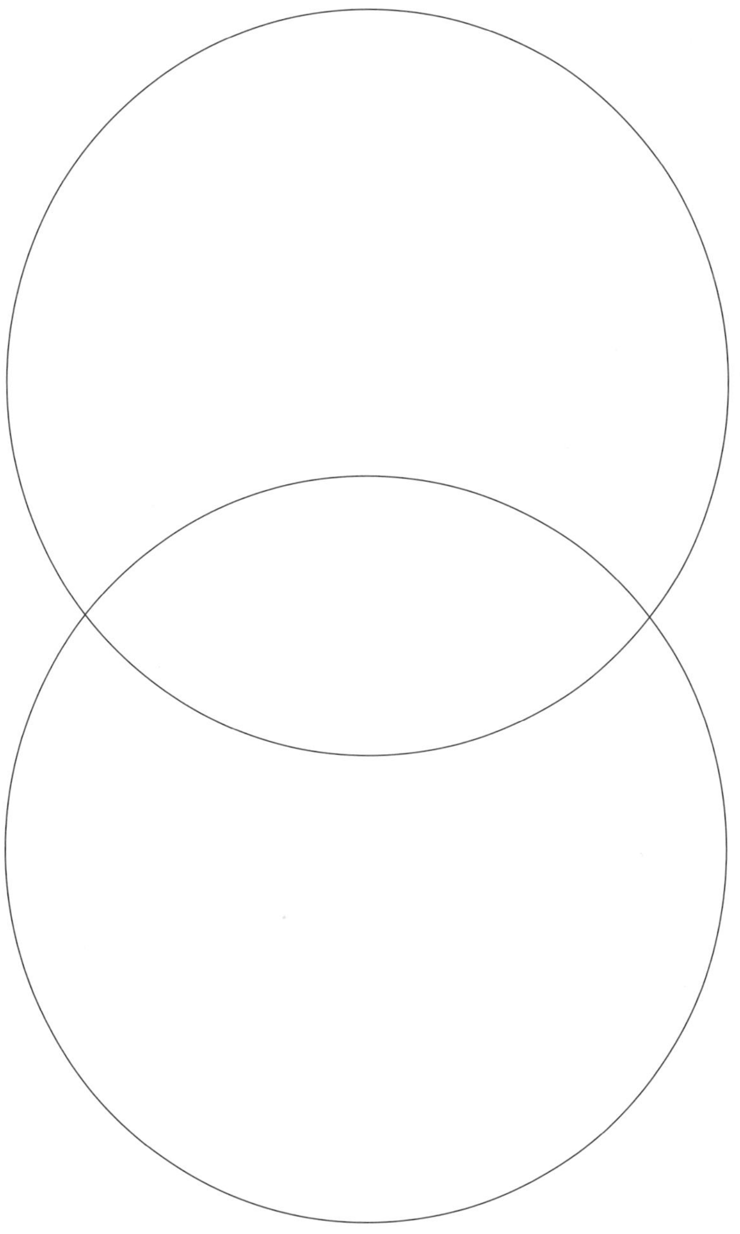

EXPLORE

Activity 8

Evaluate

Collision Data

Quick Code
ca8056s

Some students performed an investigation to prove Newton's third law of motion. They arranged two small carts of equal masses on two ramps facing each other, at a 20° incline from a distance of 40 centimeters. Then, they released the carts. As the carts collided, a sensor measured the force of Cart 1 on Cart 2, and vice versa.

At the end of the investigation, the students found that their data supported Newton's third law. **Circle** the graph that represents the data the students collected.

Graph 1

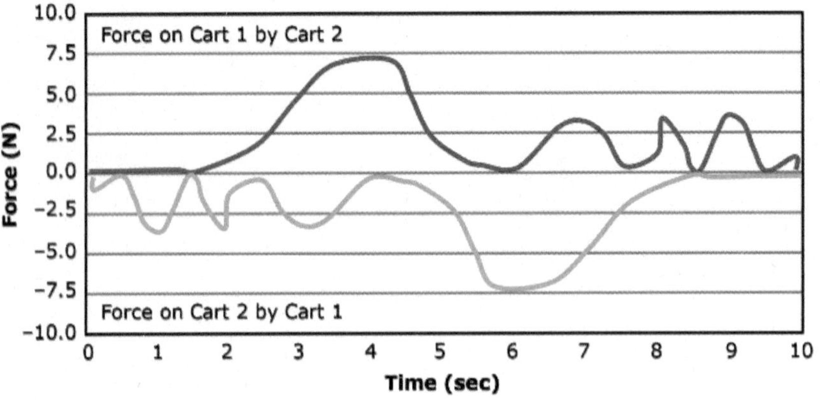

Graph 2

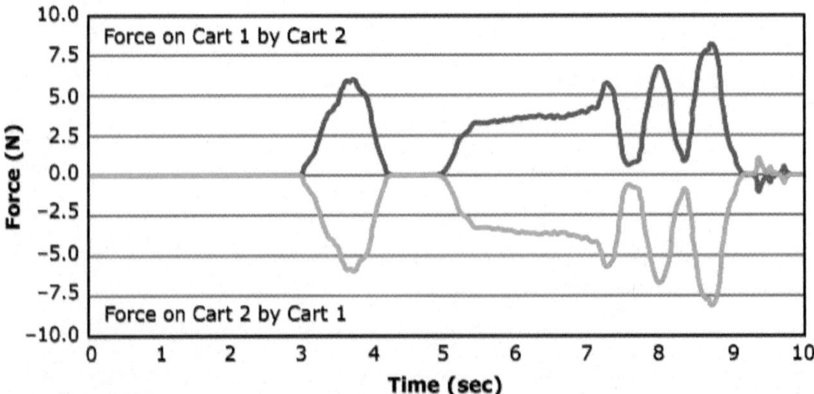

SEP **Analyzing and Interpreting Data**

Graph 3

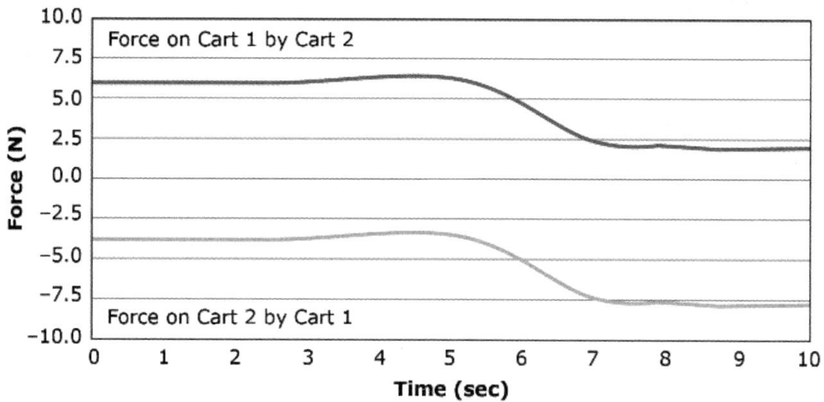

Graph 4

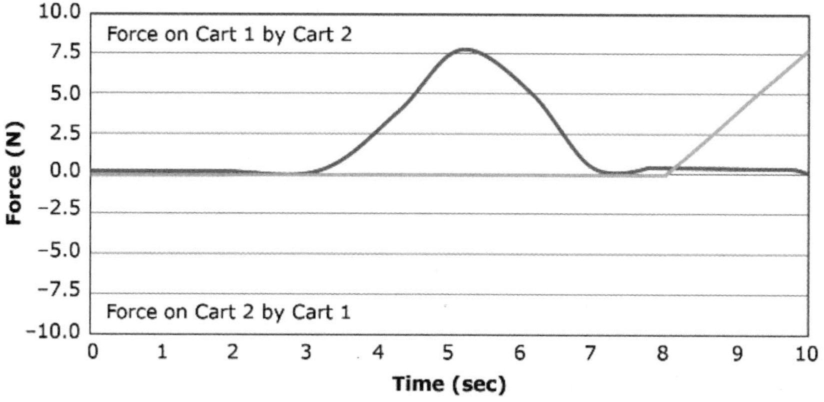

EXPLORE

How Does Energy Transfer in a Collision?

Activity 9

Observe

Persistent Energy

Quick Code
ca8057s

Go online to complete the Interactive Persistent Energy. **Read** the instructions and **click** the Continue button. **Select** the number of shooters and ducks for the marble game. (Do not choose only one shooter and one duck.) **Press** the Play button. **Observe** the interaction and **note** the amount of energy before and after the impact. Replay as necessary. **Continue** with different combinations. **Record** your results.

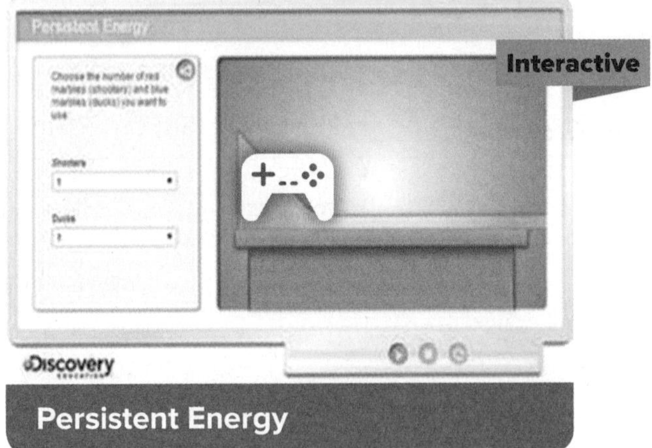

Persistent Energy

SEP Developing and Using Models

CCC Energy and Matter

Before:

After:

Changes:

Read the following and **create** an energy flow diagram on a separate sheet of paper.

In a collision, energy is transferred between objects. In the case of the Chicxulub asteroid, the asteroid had maximum kinetic energy as it approached Earth's surface. Upon impact, much of that **kinetic energy** was transferred to sound, light, and heat. The remaining kinetic energy was transferred to Earth's surface, some of which ejected miles away from the impact site. The total energy of the system remains the same due to the law of the conservation of energy.

Many collisions involving objects are similar to the asteroid example, as the two objects may compress or slightly stick together upon impact. In those systems, the kinetic energy is converted to other forms of energy. Collisions involving objects made of harder material, such as rock, more efficiently transfer kinetic energy to one another.

EXPLORE

Energy Transfer in Collisions

What happens to the energy transferred if the masses of the objects increase or the objects travel faster? We know that the kinetic energy of the object is dependent on the mass of the object as well as its velocity. If an object has a mass, *m*, and a **velocity**, *v*, then its kinetic energy, *KE*, is as follows:

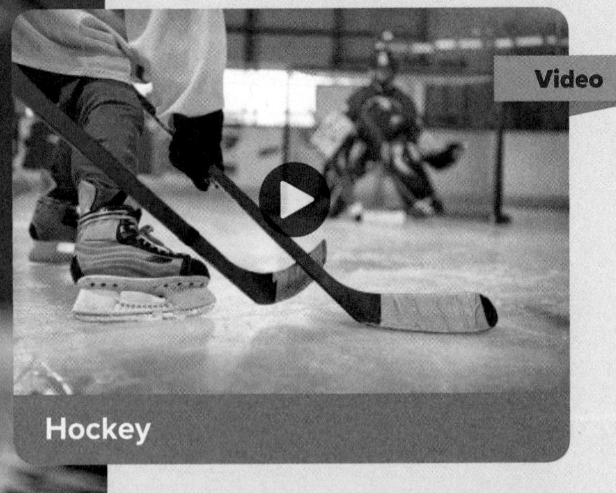

Hockey

$$KE = \frac{mv^2}{2}$$

Consider a green car sitting at a stoplight. At rest, the green car has zero kinetic energy. A yellow car, with the same mass as the green car, is moving, with kinetic energy, toward the stoplight. When the yellow car hits the green car from behind, the green car should be pushed forward with the same speed as the yellow car was traveling. Some of the kinetic energy will be transferred to sound and heat.

Car Crash

Activity 10

Analyze

Quick Code
ca8058s

Energy Transfer in Collisions

Read the text and **watch** the videos. Then, **complete** the activity that follows.

Using the formula for kinetic energy found in the text, **rank** the kinetic energy involved in the three different collisions described in the Car Crash video.

Amount of Kinetic Energy Involved	Collision Description
Most Kinetic Energy	
⬇	
Least Kinetic Energy	

EXPLORE

Activity 11

Investigate

Quick Code
ca8059s

Hands-On Investigation: Cart Collisions

In this investigation, you will collect and analyze data to learn about the linear relationship between force, mass, and acceleration in collisions.

Predict

How do you predict force, mass, and acceleration will be related in a collision?

SEP Analyzing and Interpreting Data

SEP Using Mathematics and Computational Thinking

What materials do you need? (per group)

- Air track
- Gliders of equal masses, 2
- Force sensors, 2
- Bumpers
- Force sensor software
- Weights, 50-gram

Procedure

Position two gliders on an air track as shown.

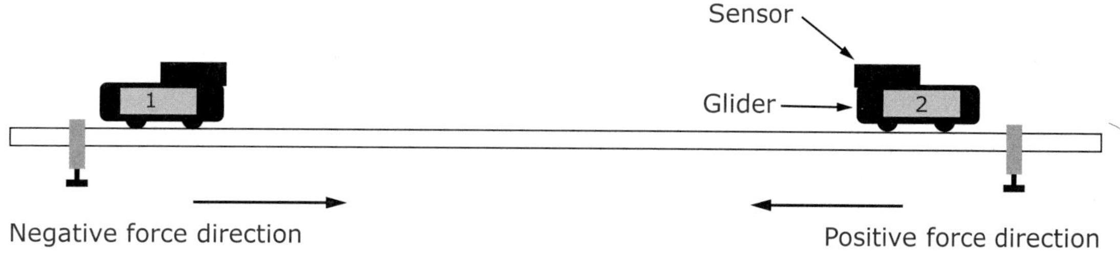

EXPLORE

What do you think will happen in each scenario? Complete the "Force Predictions" portion of the table with your predictions.

Glider 1	Glider 2	Mass	Force Predictions	Observations
Moving	Stationary	Equal		
Moving	Moving	Equal		
Moving, with 100 g extra mass	Stationary	Unequal		
Moving, with 100 g extra mass	Moving	Unequal		

Part 1

Use your hand to launch glider 1 toward glider 2. Observe the collision. What do you notice? Observe the sensor data. Complete the correct "Observation" portion of the table.

Part 2

Place the gliders at either end of the track. With a partner, use your hands to launch the gliders toward each other at the same time. Observe the collision. What do you notice? Observe the sensor data. Complete the correct "Observation" portion of the table.

EXPLORE

Part 3

Place two 50-gram weights onto the pins of glider 1. Place the gliders in the previous "stationary" position. Use your hands to launch glider 1 toward glider 2. Observe the collision. What do you notice? Observe the sensor data. Complete the correct "Observation" portion of the table.

Part 4

Place the gliders at either end of the track. With a partner, use your hands to launch the gliders toward each other at the same time. Observe the collision. What do you notice? Observe the sensor data. Complete the correct "Observation" portion of the table.

Reflect

Use the data and your observations to compare the collisions you created: Stationary vs. Moving. What does the data show about the forces exerted by each glider at point of impact?

Use the data and your observations to compare the collisions you created when one glider was weighted. What does the data show about the forces exerted by each glider at point of impact?

EXPLORE

What is the relationship between mass and force in a collision?

Do your tests prove Newton's third law of motion? How?

Activity 12

Evaluate

Quick Code
ca8060s

Preventing Asteroid Impact

EXPLORE

NASA uses ground-based and infrared telescopes to observe and detect NEOs that may pose a threat to Earth. Should one get close, there are two promising techniques to prevent an impact:

- Change the velocity of the asteroid by hitting it with an object to slow it down.
- Place a mass near it to use gravitational force to pull the asteroid off its path.

Any course of action would need to consider several factors such as composition, properties, amount of time before impact, and relative velocity of the asteroid.

Which solution do you think would be most effective? **Explain** your answer and **provide** evidence for your claim. What are some drawbacks to your chosen approach?

SEP Constructing Explanations and Designing Solutions

Now, **move** to the side of the classroom representing the design solution you think would be most effective. In small groups, **discuss** your explanation for selecting your solution. **Add** your group's thoughts to the four "W" questions as you rotate around your half of the room.

Why?

What?

When?

Where?

EXPLORE

Activity 13

Solve Problems

Quick Code
ca8062s

Design a Bumper

Read the text and examine the images. Then, **complete** the activity that follows.

We're Walking, We're Walking...

A survey conducted by the Federal Highway Administration found that about 51 percent of Americans walk on a regular basis. Most people walk for social or recreational reasons, such as walking a dog or visiting a friend. Others walk to run errands or to go to work or school. Walking is good for your health, good for the environment, and good for your wallet... gasoline costs money, but walking is free.

Pedestrian and Motor Vehicle Impacts

Walkers must share the streets with motor vehicles, and sometimes that leads to pedestrian injuries or even death. The National Highway Traffic Safety Administration reported that in the United States in 2015 there were approximately 70,000 pedestrians injured in traffic crashes with cars. That's almost 200 people per day!

In the past, education and traffic regulations have been used to reduce the amount of car-related pedestrian accidents. In the latter half of the 1900s, engineers turned

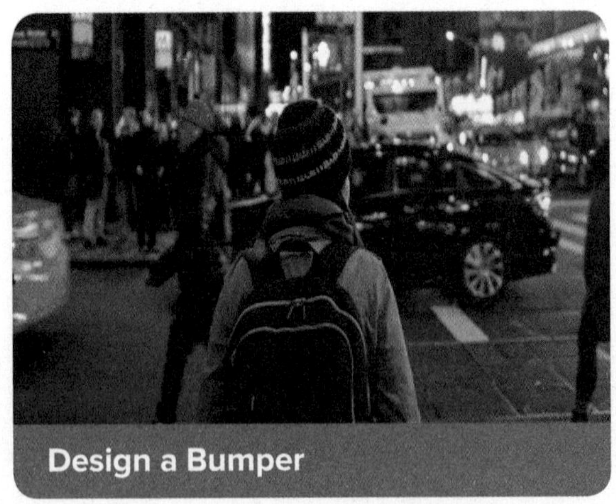

Design a Bumper

SEP Constructing Explanations and Designing Solutions

toward vehicle design as a way to lower the likelihood of an injury or death in a crash. They looked at ways to redesign bumpers, hoods, and windshields to mitigate impacts to legs, torsos, and heads. For example, in the 1990s, Europe and Japan introduced regulations that motor vehicle designs include features that reduce lower leg injuries in pedestrian impacts. Automakers tested new concepts in simulations where cars with different bumper designs would be struck by a model of a person's leg. They would then analyze how much the leg model bent upon impact. A bend in the knee greater than 15° would result in injury to the knee joint.

EXPLORE

What Are Bumpers Made Of?

The purpose of a bumper is to absorb impact in a crash, thereby protecting the vehicle from maximum damage and expensive repairs. They are typically made of a plastic cover; a rigid reinforcement bar made of a hard material, such as metal, fiberglass, or plastic; and a material to absorb the energy of a collision, such as foam, an "egg crate," or a plastic honeycomb. There is also usually some space between the reinforcement bar and the body of the car.

Bumper Parts

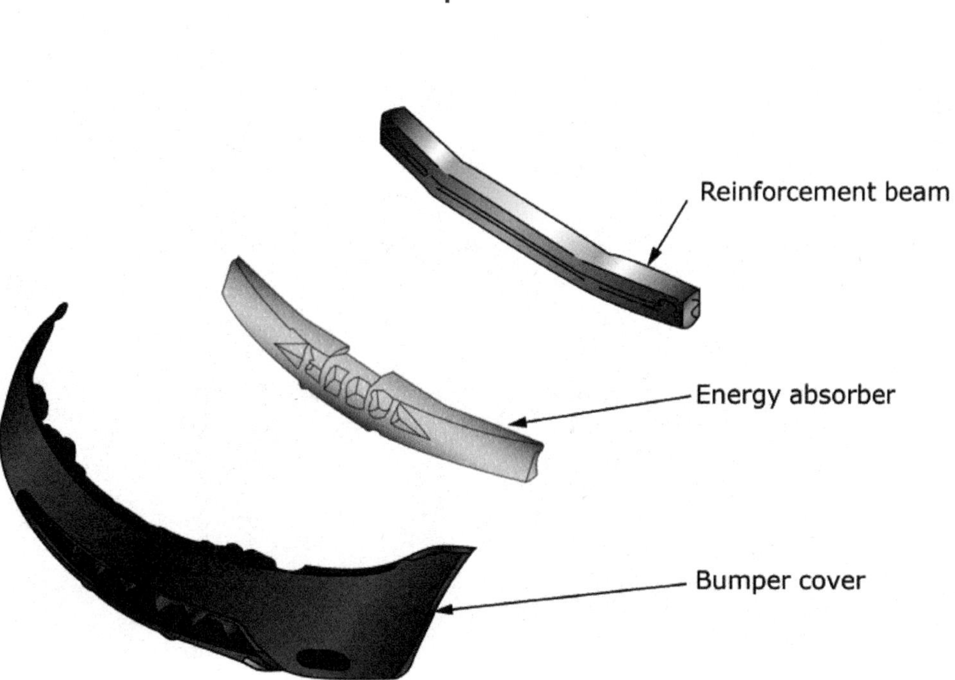

How Do Bumpers Work?

Newton's third law of motion tells us for every action, there is an equal and opposite reaction. In a motor vehicle collision, bumpers are able to take on some of the energy transferred back to the car upon impact. The bumper's absorbing material will crush or collapse, and the reinforcement bar will distribute the collision energy. These actions extend the time of a collision, reducing the impact force on its parts and the people inside.

Pedestrian Protection

While bumpers are designed to protect the vehicle to which it is attached, it is not feasible to wrap a pedestrian in absorbent material or reinforced steel for protection from cars. So, how can pedestrians be better protected during a motor vehicle collision? Is it possible to design a bumper so that it protects both the person walking and the car?

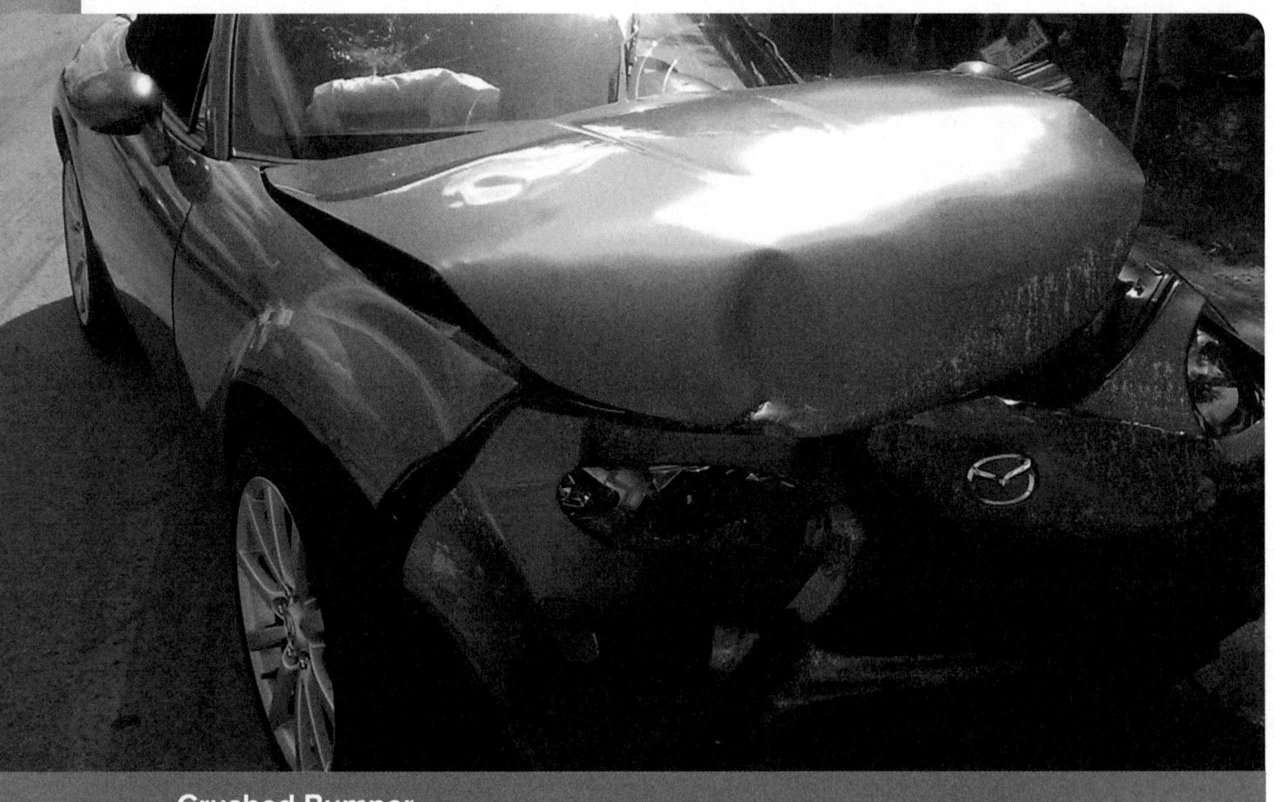

Crushed Bumper

Engineers have tried to answer this question by designing a bumper that cushions a pedestrian while also protecting the vehicle. They have tried crafting bumpers with different materials such as:

- absorbers made from different foams or plastics
- air-filled cushions
- a more flexible reinforcement beam
- a bumper that pushes out when an impact is detected
- crushable cans attached to the reinforcement beam
- bars attached to the front of a main bumper

The bumper position is also important. It must be placed to provide enough support to the main bumper, so a pedestrian's knee does not bend too much during impact. Some methods have included these modifications:

- material placed so that it sits below the main bumper
- a low bumper that pushes out when impact is detected
- a low bumper that pushes out when pressure on the main bumper is detected
- material placed above the main bumper

Protecting pedestrian safety extends beyond the United States as the number of cars on the road increases worldwide. You will work in teams of four to design a bumper for a car that will minimize lower leg injury. Then, you will measure the angle of bend in a lower leg model to determine the effectiveness of your bumper.

You and your team will follow the steps on the Engineering Design Process sheet to design your bumper. Discuss your design with your team, deciding on your approach and independent variables. You may design your bumper with variations of a single material, by mixing materials, or by varying the position of a design on the car. You will be allowed three trials to meet the bumper design regulations of a 15° bend or less in the knee upon impact.

Requirements

- You may use any combination of bumper materials to create the bumper: egg carton, paper tubes, bubble wrap, sponge, straws.
- Use rubber bands or tape to secure the bumper to the car.
- The bumper may not add more than 100 grams to the mass of the model car.
- The bumper may not extend more than 6 centimeters in front of the car.
- The bumper may not impede the motion of your car on the ramp.
- Your ramp must be at least 40 centimeters long and raised to a 30° angle from the horizontal.
- The front of your bumper will be placed on the 40-centimeter mark on the ramp before launch.

Procedure

1. **Twist** together three pipe cleaners to create a model leg. **Use** clay to hold the bottom of the leg while a team member holds the top with one finger. Clay should not contact the car upon impact. **Place** the model leg 30 centimeters from the end of the ramp.
2. **Place** the front of the bumper at the 40-centimeter mark on the ramp and **release** the car toward the leg.
3. **Use** a protractor to measure degree of bend in the pipe cleaners. **Record** your results.
4. **Revisit** your design and **make** and **record** any necessary changes. **Straighten** the model leg before conducting another test and **repeat** steps 1–3 two more times.

Record your results in a chart like the one that follows.

Bumper Design	Degree of Leg Bend

EXPLORE

Design Details

Describe your bumper design process and how it works. **Explain** which variable you tested (material type, location of bumper, and configuration of bumper material) and how you modified it in your test. **Explain** why you chose those variables, relating your choice to what you know about how bumpers work in a collision.

Energy Flow Diagram

Sketch your car bumper design solution, including design details and labels to show how each component works. On your sketch, use arrows to show how your bumper will interact with the collision energy to cushion the pedestrian upon impact.

EXPLORE

Elements of Effective Bumper Design

Review your design solution and **observe** other teams' ideas. Based on your observations, which models were the most successful at preventing injury to the model leg? Which features made them effective? **List** two to three features of your own design that could be modified to improve it.

EXPLORE

Activity 14

Record Evidence

Quick Code
ca8061s

Meteorites Hitting Earth

As you worked through this lesson, you investigated and gathered evidence about colliding objects. Now, take another look at the video Meteorites Hitting Earth, which you first saw in Engage.

How has your understanding of the video Meteorites Hitting Earth changed?

Read the Can You Explain? question from the beginning of this lesson.

Can You Explain?

How much energy would an asteroid impact transfer to Earth's surface?

SEP Constructing Explanations and Designing Solutions

Plan a scientific explanation to answer the Can You Explain? or a question of your own. Recall that a scientific explanation contains three elements: a scientific claim, evidence to support the claim, and reasoning that connects the evidence to the claim. Use this planning chart to develop your scientific explanation:

Scientific Explanation Planning Chart
What is my claim?
What data from my investigations can I use to support my claim?
What reliable evidence from the text and/or videos can I use as evidence?

EXPLAIN

Which scientific ideas, principles, and/or laws apply to my explanation?

Now, **use** the information in your planning chart to **write** your scientific explanation.

Scientific Explanation (Explanation = Claim + Evidence + Logical Reasoning)	
Directions: Create a scientific explanation for the question. This combines the claim that was made, the evidence that was collected, and a justification for why the evidence supports the claim (logical reasoning). The explanation should contain clear thoughts and accurate scientific vocabulary.	Key Components: • Uses precise and accurate language • Uses scientific vocabulary • Provides clear, logical thoughts • Uses evidence and reasoning to support the claim

EXPLAIN

STEM in Action

Activity 15

Analyze

Quick Code
ca8065s

Careers and Nonplanetary Objects

Read the following passage and **watch** the video. Before you read and watch, **think** about how you could use social media posts to inform people about an asteroid impact. What would people need to know?

Careers and Nonplanetary Objects

Asteroids have hit Earth many times in the past. We can see evidence of this in the presence of large craters, rare elements such as iridium, and major extinctions in the fossil record. Scientists predict that a large impact could occur about once every million years. Even smaller impacts could have devastating consequences for countries and regions. This is why scientists have developed special instruments to detect asteroids that may be on a collision course with Earth.

Astronomers at the Arecibo Observatory in Puerto Rico use a radio telescope to track nonplanetary objects. The radar tells them where an asteroid is and how far from Earth it is. Repeated measurements allow scientists to calculate how fast an asteroid is moving, its direction, and to predict if and when it will strike Earth.

This data collection and evaluation process continues around the clock. It requires scientists, engineers, and computer analysts to keep this operation running.

Scientists and engineers are also working on ways to avoid collisions between asteroids and Earth. The latest idea involves using a spacecraft to exert a gravitational force on an asteroid. This maneuver would slow the asteroid down enough to miss its intercept with Earth. The force of gravity between two interacting objects depends on their masses and the distance between them. Therefore, scientists must make careful calculations to predict exactly what would need to happen in each individual case. Rest assured that NASA and other space agencies around the world have world-class computer modelers working on such problems. Can you imagine having such a job?

Preparing For Large Impacts

ELABORATE

Draft three social media posts:

- The first post should inform people about the possibility of an impact from an asteroid.
- The second post should inform people about the work of scientists to predict the impact.
- The third post should inform people about additional information scientists can find out from researching asteroids.

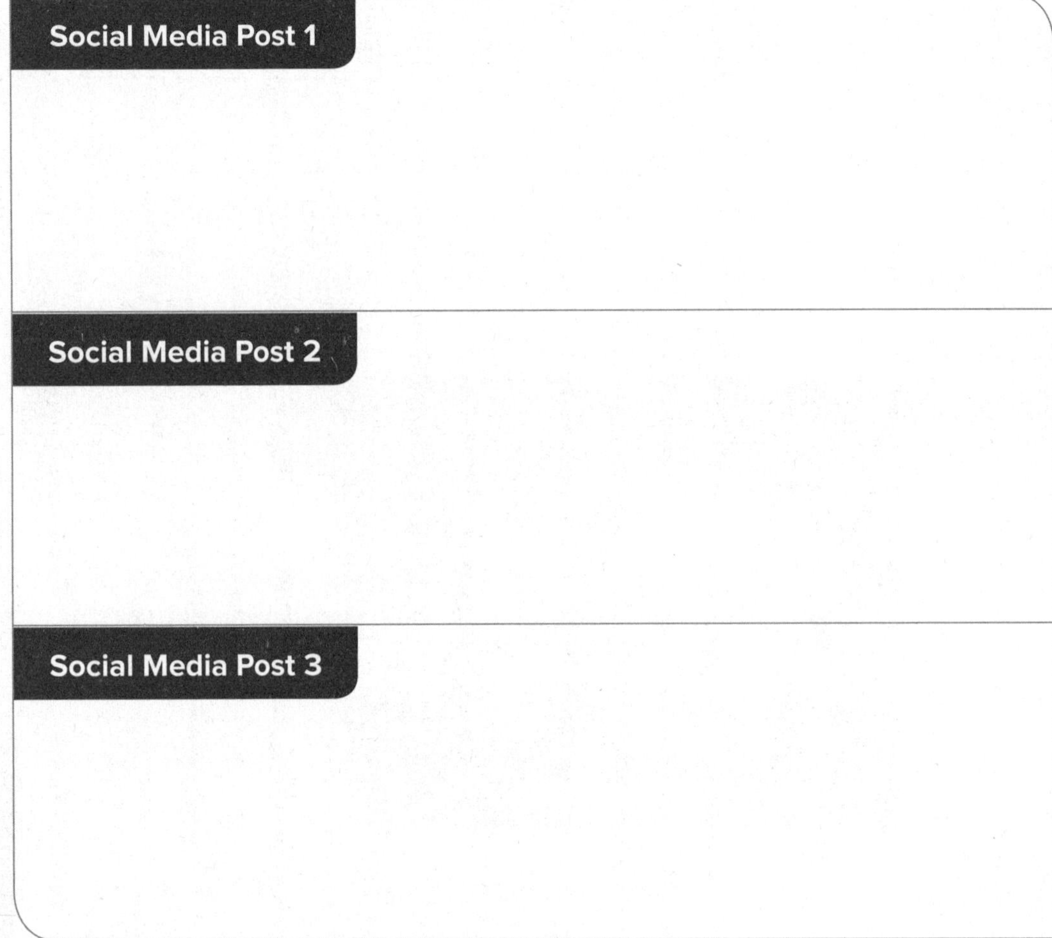

Social Media Post 1
Social Media Post 2
Social Media Post 3

Predicting Planet-Asteroid Collisions

This diagram shows the orbital paths of the planets and several groups of asteroids in the vicinity of Earth.

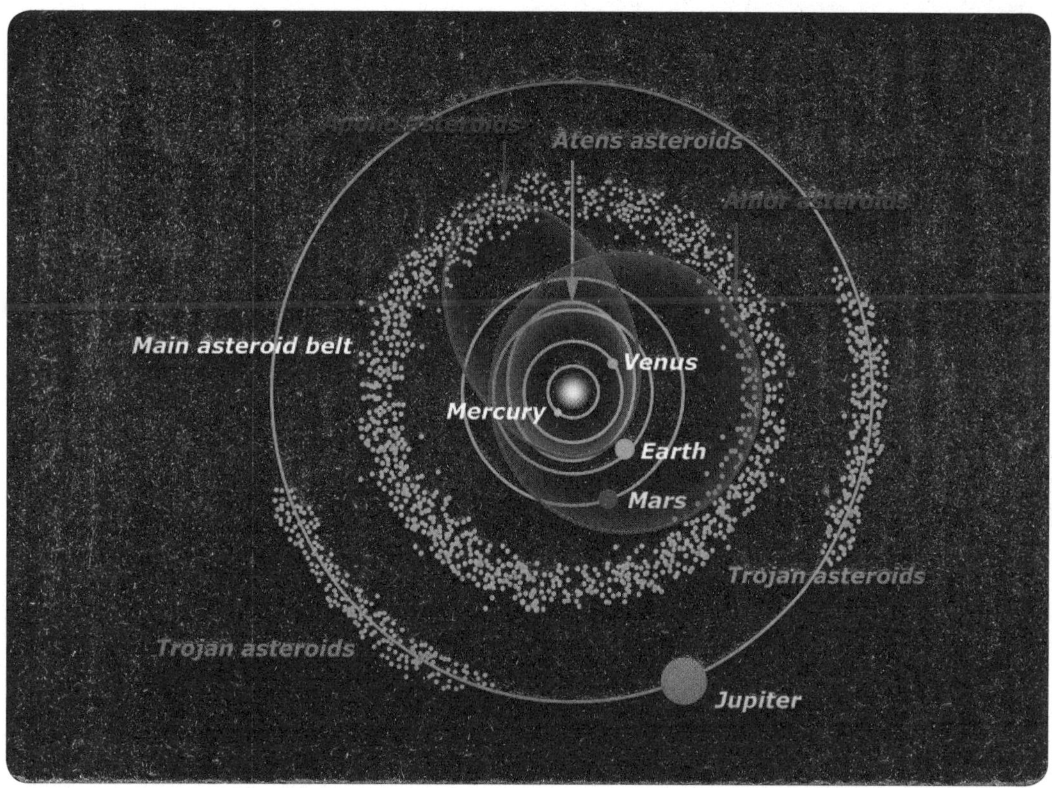

Under each of the asteroid groups listed, **write** the planets it might threaten. **Choose** only the planets shown on the diagram.

Apollo

____

Amor

____

Atens

____

Trojan

____

ELABORATE

Activity 16

Concept Review

Quick Code
ca8066s

Review: Colliding Objects

Now that you have completed the objectives for this concept, review the core ideas you have learned. Record some of the core ideas in the space provided.

Core Ideas

Talk with a Group

Now, think about the asteroid impact crater video you saw in Get Started. Discuss how what you've learned about colliding objects can help you understand an asteroid colliding with Earth.

EVALUATE

Solve Problems

Quick Code
ca8068s

Unit Project: Prepare for Impact

Will humans have time to prepare for a large asteroid collision on Earth? **Read** the passage, and then **read** the description of the project.

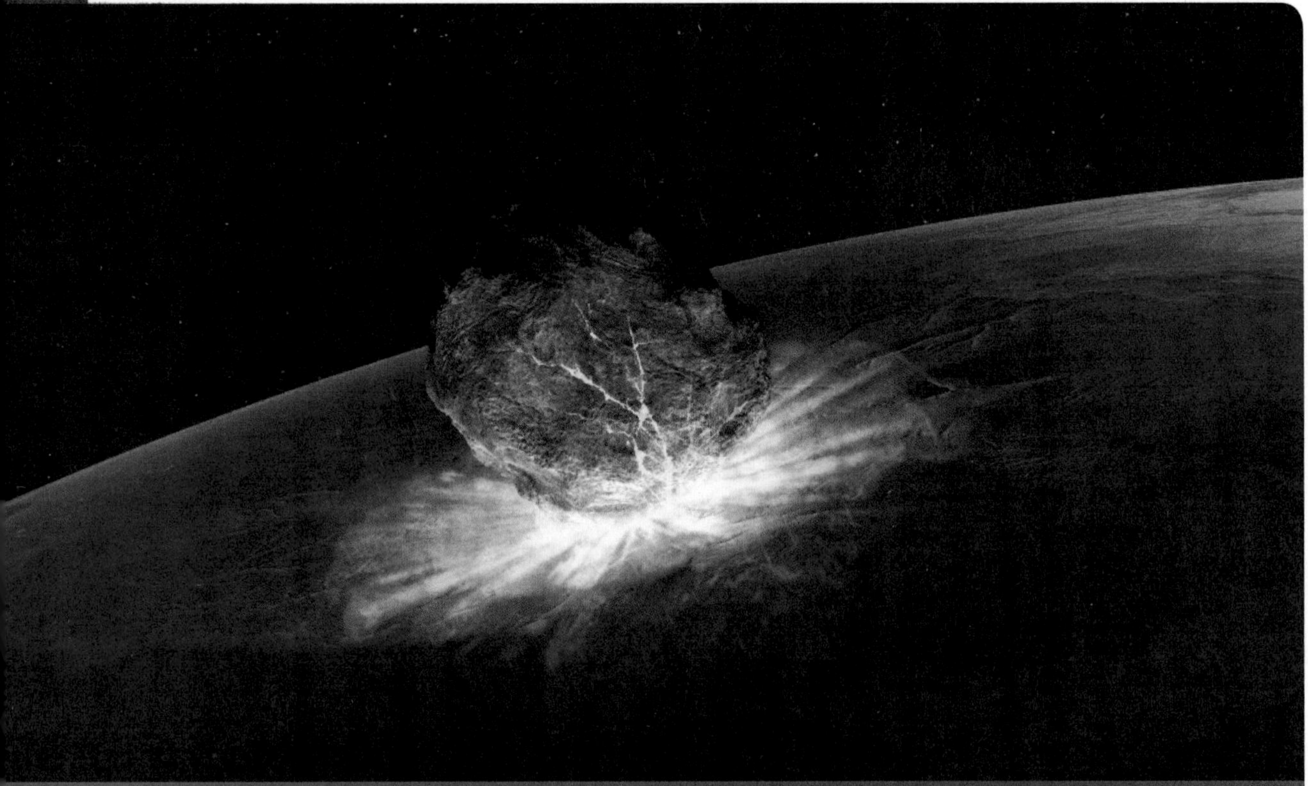

Asteroid Hitting Planet Earth

SEP Analyzing and Interpreting Data

SEP Obtaining, Evaluating, and Communicating Information

CCC Cause and Effect

Prepare for Impact

Small asteroids pass nearby every few weeks, and small fragments fall to Earth as meteorites on a daily basis. However, if a large asteroid veers toward our planet, the Planetary Defense Coordination Office (PDCO) is on watch. They use technology to track near-Earth objects, or NEOs that could impact Earth. Telescopes and other instruments help them understand an asteroid's size, shape, rotation, orbit, and physical composition. They use that data to assess any potential risks.

What would it take to produce a catastrophic collision on Earth? A very large asteroid. The PDCO provides some rough estimates about the size of a meteor and how much of Earth it would affect. For example, objects larger than 0.14 kilometers would cause damage within a region of Earth such as a country, or several countries, or a large area of the ocean. Asteroids larger than 0.3 kilometers in diameter would affect most of the planet. Asteroids larger than 1 kilometer would cause effects worldwide. The impact at Chicxulub, Mexico, around 65.5 million years ago is believed to have had worldwide effects on climate and led to mass extinctions. Large asteroid impacts are a part of Earth's past and will be a part of its future. For this reason, the NASA Jet Propulsion Laboratory (JPL) in California maintains the Sentry Impact Risk Data table. Velocity, diameter, magnitude, and impact probability are calculated for nearby asteroids. Then, they are assigned an impact hazard rating on a 0–10 scale. The Impact Risk Data table lists any object with the potential for a future Earth impact event over the next 100 years along with its rating.

This project requires you to use what you have learned about Newton's laws of motion and impact craters to determine if there is enough time to prepare for a potential asteroid collision. You will perform calculations of velocity, kinetic energy, and force using data gathered about an asteroid. Then, you will consider what is known about the asteroid that struck Earth at Chicxulub. You will compare it with this new, hypothetical asteroid threat.

Are We Prepared?

The Jet Propulsion Laboratory has detected an NEO that is headed toward Earth. The PDCO needs to issue a press release to warn those who will be affected by the asteroid.

Using the data gathered by JPL in the table, **create** a press release to inform the public about:

1. Characteristics of the asteroid
2. The asteroid's velocity in kilometers per day
3. The asteroid's kinetic energy in $kg{\cdot}km^2/day^2$
4. The asteroid's force, once it enters the atmosphere and is affected by Earth's gravity
5. How this situation compares with the impact of the asteroid at Chicxulub, Mexico, 65.5 million years ago

Data Gathered by Jet Propulsion Laboratory, NASA:

- Asteroid name: 2018 MP34
- Mass = 1.6×10^{11} kg
- Diameter = 0.49 km

Time from Detection (days)	Distance from Earth
0	24.6×10^6 km
2	20.2×10^6 km
5	13.6×10^6 km
6	11.6×10^6 km

Calculate the velocity, kinetic energy, and force. **Write** your calculations.

Write your press release in the space provided.

UNIT

2

Moving Planets

A Diamond Planet

Quick Code
ca8250s

What would you do if you discovered an entire planet made of diamond? Scientists use technology to collect data about planetary objects within and beyond our solar system. Though the composition of exoplanets is different from Earth, they display orbital behaviors that provide evidence that they also experience gravitational forces. In this unit, you will explore the impact of gravitational forces on objects in our solar system, as well as other noncontact forces used to move objects on Earth.

Guiding Questions

1. What causes the cyclical changes in the appearance of the moon?
2. How can an object influence the motion of another object without touching it?
3. Does Earth's force of gravity attract other objects equally?

A Diamond Planet

Solve Problems

Quick Code
ca8251s

Unit Project: Exoplanet Follow-Up

Thinking About Solutions

How can we confirm the existence of an exoplanet and further explore it?

You must help scientists who are designing a new technological tool to confirm the existence of the exoplanet nearest Earth, Proxima B. They have already sent tiny probes and a telescope to get direct images. Before moving forward, **determine** which problem(s) should be solved by the new tool. Then, **develop** solutions to those problems and decide how you can optimize your design.

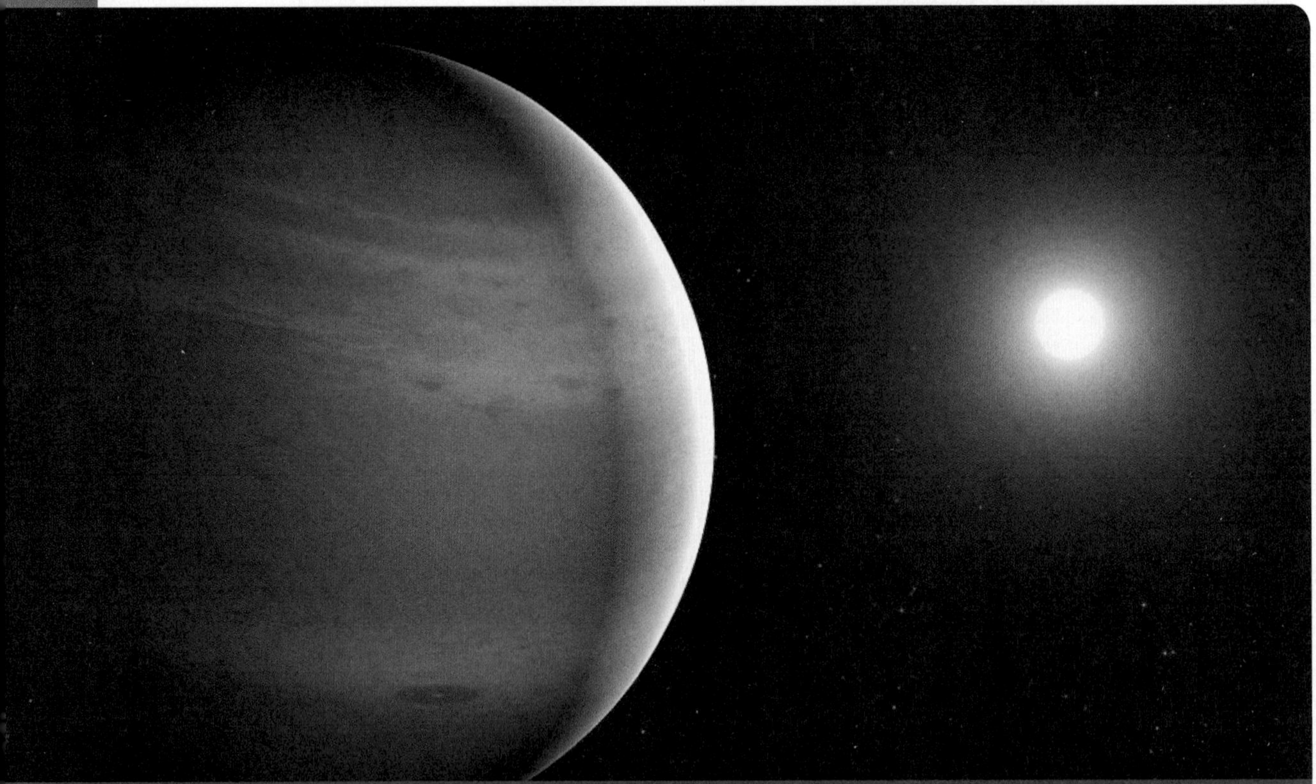

Planet GJ 436b

Use the graphic organizer to sort your ideas.

Define the Problem

Brainstorm Solutions

CONCEPT

2.1

Observing Planetary Objects

Student Objectives

By the end of this lesson:

- [ ] I can develop scale models of the solar system based on scientific evidence.
- [ ] I can analyze and interpret data to describe patterns in the characteristics of solar system objects.
- [ ] I can develop models of the Earth-sun-moon system that describe cyclical patterns of lunar phases and eclipses of the sun and moon.
- [ ] I can analyze and interpret data to describe patterns in the movements of solar system objects and to predict future eclipses.

Key Vocabulary

Celsius, galaxy, gas, heat, hydrogen, light, light year, magnify, nebulae, optical, star, sun, telescope, universe

Quick Code
ca8253s

Activity 1

Can You Explain?

How do we obtain data about the properties of exoplanets and objects in our solar system?

Quick Code
ca8254s

Activity 2
Ask Questions

Quick Code
ca8255s

Exoplanets

Scientists use data collection tools to discover new information about objects in our solar system.

What types of tools and technology do scientists use to learn more about objects outside of our solar system?

Let's Investigate Exoplanets

Activity 3
Analyze

Quick Code
ca8256s

ENGAGE

Exoplanet Remote Sensing

Read the text to answer the question: What types of tools and technology do scientists use to learn more about objects outside of our solar system?

Exoplanet Remote Sensing

Scientists have been designing tools to extend scientific understanding of space for many years. As technology has evolved, the complexity of devices designed to expand our understanding of space has evolved. This has resulted in an ever-growing body of knowledge about space exploration. Instruments scientists use to observe and detect distant objects in space are called remote sensing devices.

Telescopes are the primary remote sensing tools scientists use to study the **universe**. While telescopes work in different ways, they all operate on the same basic principle. Telescopes gather, focus, and **magnify** electromagnetic waves. Some remote sensing instruments are located on Earth's surface. However, Earth's atmosphere can absorb and distort light and other forms of electromagnetic radiation. This absorption and distortion can decrease the quality of the data being collected.

SEP **Obtaining, Evaluating, and Communicating Information**

Some forms of electromagnetic radiation are absorbed more easily than others. Radio waves are absorbed very little. This means that they pass right through the atmosphere. However, dust and gases in the atmosphere distort visible light, gamma rays, X-rays, and many wavelengths of infrared and ultraviolet radiation. One way of dealing with this problem is to build observatories at high elevations.

Astronomers have also launched space telescopes that orbit Earth outside of the atmosphere. This mostly eliminates data distortion issues caused by Earth's atmosphere. As a result, space telescopes can produce clearer images than those on Earth's surface. Because radio waves are not distorted by gases and dust in Earth's atmosphere, radio telescopes are usually located on Earth's surface and do not need to be launched into space.

Scientists have designed other remote sensing devices. These include probes and satellites. Probes have traveled to planets, comets, and asteroids in our solar system. Some of these probes have even traveled beyond the edges of our solar system.

Most satellites do not travel far into space. Instead, they orbit planets and moons. Humans have launched thousands of satellites into Earth's orbit.

What types of tools and technology do scientists use to learn more about objects outside of our solar system?

ENGAGE

Activity 4

Evaluate

Quick Code
ca8257s

What Do You Already Know About Observing Planetary Objects?

Apparent Sizes

The moon is significantly smaller than the sun. Why is the moon able to fully block the sun from our view on Earth?

Orbits

Describe the orbits of Earth and the moon. In your descriptions, **include** the distance from the sun or Earth and the amount of time it takes Earth and the moon to complete their orbits.

Moon: Facts or Fiction?

For each statement in the chart, **decide** whether you think it is true or false and **check** the appropriate box.

	True	False
The moon is dark all of the time on its far side.		
The moon is sometimes visible during the day.		
The moon revolves around Earth, and Earth revolves around the sun.		
The moon glows because it reflects light from the sun.		

ENGAGE

What Are the Parts of a Planet?

Read the descriptions. Next to each description, write the layer of a planet that it describes.

core	surface	atmosphere	moon

A layer of gases surrounding a planet

____

The material at the center of a planet

____

A natural satellite that orbits a planet

____

The outermost layer of a planet

____

How Do We Observe Our Solar System from Earth's Surface?

Activity 5

Observe

Quick Code ca8258s

Planets of the Solar System

The solar system includes eight planets: Mercury, Venus, Earth, Mars, Jupiter, Saturn, Uranus, and Neptune. They share some features and differ in others. **Write** in the chart three questions you have about them. Then, **use** the following interactive to write the answers and **make** a sketch of the solar system.

Questions	Answers

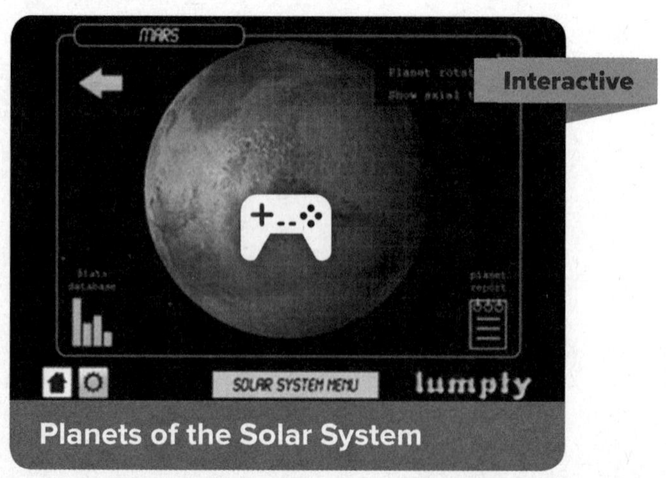

Planets of the Solar System

EXPLORE

Solar System

SEP Asking Questions and Defining Problems

CCC Scale, Proportion, and Quantity

Activity 6

Reason

Quick Code
ca8259s

Model of Outer Planets

In this investigation, you will work with a group to create a model of the planets in the solar system.

Procedure

First, go online to complete the interactive.

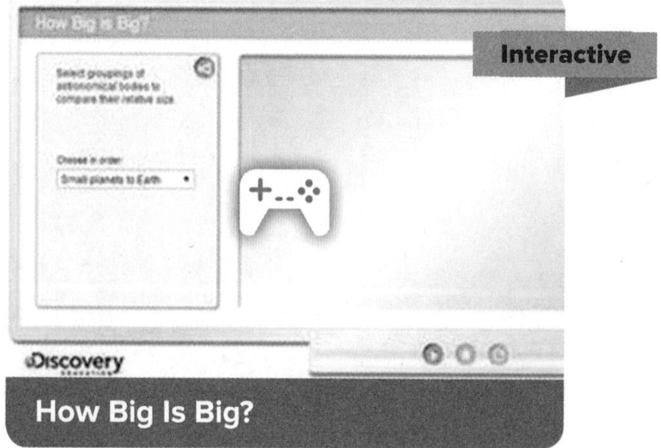

How Big Is Big?

How can you model the relative sizes of the outer planets and Earth?

____

____

____

____

____

____

SEP Developing and Using Models

CCC Scale, Proportion, and Quantity

What materials do you need? (per group)

- Tennis balls
- Golf balls
- Basketballs
- Soccer balls
- Softballs
- Marbles, $\frac{5}{8}$ in.
- Balloons
- Metersticks

EXPLORE

1. Look at a variety of round objects and imagine a model of the solar system made of them.
2. Sketch your model to represent the scale of objects in the solar system. Write an explanation to describe the relationship of objects to one another.
3. Take into consideration both their relative sizes and distances from the sun.
4. Then, build the model using the same objects and the sketch for reference.

Solar System Model

Reflect

What are the advantages of your model?

What are the limitations of your model?

What role do models play in science?

EXPLORE

Activity 7

Reason

Quick Code
ca8260s

Earth's Cyclical Orbit

In this investigation, you will sketch the cyclical changes in Earth's orbit that result in cyclical changes in Earth's climate over long periods of time.

What materials do you need? (per group)

- Copy of worksheet: Earth's Cyclical Orbit
- Pencils
- Metric ruler
- Compass
- Colored pencils

Procedure

1. Use the ruler to measure and draw the lengths of the major and minor axes of Earth's orbit on the diagram that follows.
2. Then, place the point of the compass on the "X" and the pencil end on the dashed line at the top and draw a circle; it will represent the most circular orbit of Earth.
3. Finally, use the ruler and the blue colored pencil to mark the section of Earth's orbit at which Earth is farthest from the sun.

SEP Planning and Carrying Out Investigations

CCC Scale, Proportion, and Quantity

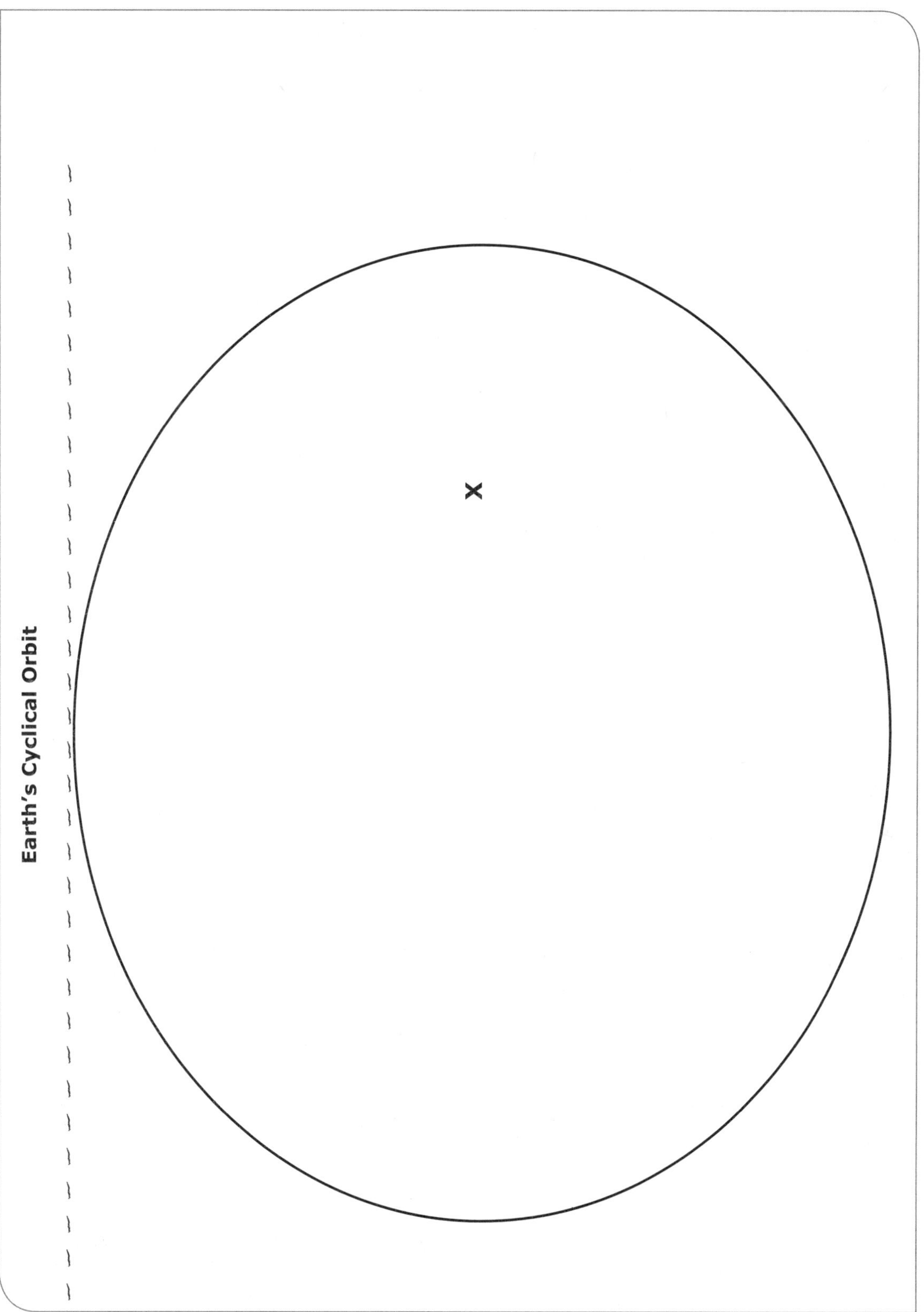
Earth's Cyclical Orbit
X

Reflect

How does the amount of solar energy change as Earth orbits the sun?

How does the change in solar energy impact Earth's environment?

Activity 8

Analyze

Quick Code
ca8261s

Moon Viewed from Earth

Read the following text and **view** the videos and image. Pay attention to the changes of the moon over time. Then, **answer** the question that follows.

EXPLORE

Moon Viewed from Earth

For thousands of years, people have been gazing up at the moon in wonder. Some cultures have myths about a giant rabbit that lives on the moon. Other cultures talk about the "man in the moon" because they perceive a likeness of a face in the surface of a full moon. There are more than 150 moons in our solar system. However, without the use of technology, we can only observe Earth's moon from the surface of Earth.

The last time you saw the moon, what did it look like? Did it appear as a full circle of **light**; a dark, barely visible disc; a thin, illuminated slice; or something in between? Did you see the moon close to the horizon or high in the sky? You have probably noticed that the moon's appearance changes from one night to the next and that its position in the sky changes throughout the night. You may also have observed that this changing appearance follows a predictable pattern. The relative positions of the sun, the moon, and Earth change the appearance of the moon.

Video

Moons in the Solar System

Full Moon

The moon itself does not emit its own light. It shines because its highly reflective surface, made of the light- and dark-colored rock and lunar soil, or regolith, reflects the sun's light back to Earth. Sunlight only reaches the half of the moon's surface that is facing the sun. The phase of the moon depends on its position relative to the sun and Earth.

Not only does the apparent shape of the moon change, but its position in the sky also changes. This is also a result of the moon's movement in space. The change in position over the course of one night is a result of Earth's rotation. Because Earth rotates from west to east, everything in the sky, including the moon, appears to rise in the east and set in the west. Although the time at which the sun rises and sets varies little from day to day, the moon rises and sets at noticeably different times. Because the moon completes one revolution around Earth in 29.5 days, it appears to move eastward about 13 to 15 degrees along its orbit of Earth each day. As a result, the moon appears to rise about an hour later each night than the night before.

Phases of the Moon

The moon takes about 27.3 days to orbit Earth. A full lunar cycle, however, takes 29.5 days. This difference between the moon's orbiting time and a full cycle of phases is because the moon is orbiting Earth as Earth is orbiting the sun. As a result, the moon must travel a bit farther around Earth to catch up with its relative starting position.

Why does the surface of the moon seem to change over time?

SEP **Obtaining, Evaluating, and Communicating Information**

EXPLORE

Activity 9

Reason

Modeling Phases of the Moon

Quick Code
ca8262s

In this investigation, you and your group will create a model to demonstrate the way in which Earth's moon changes in appearance during its cycle.

What materials do you need? (per group)

- Pencils
- Foam balls, 3 in.
- Lamp without a shade
- Dark room
- Paper
- Markers
- Computers
- Frosted light bulb

SEP Developing and Using Models

CCC Patterns

Procedure

1. In your group, find a volunteer to represent Earth and a volunteer to serve as record keeper.
2. Stick a pencil into the foam ball, representing the moon, and place the lamp at eye level in the middle of the room, representing the sun.
3. Turn off the room light and turn on the lamp.
4. The "Earth student" faces the lamp and holds the foam ball at arm's length, trying different heights. The record keeper sketches the positions of the three elements and takes notes of how the "moon" appears to "Earth" and the rest of the group.
5. Then, the "Earth student" turns slowly 90° counterclockwise four times. Each time, the record keeper makes new sketches and notations.
6. Then, use the computer to collect information about each phase of the moon, including corresponding labels, and build a full cycle model based on the following chart.

Phase of the Moon	Image

Use the image as a reference to **create** drawings of the moon phases for your model. **Place** the drawings on your model on the corresponding phase.

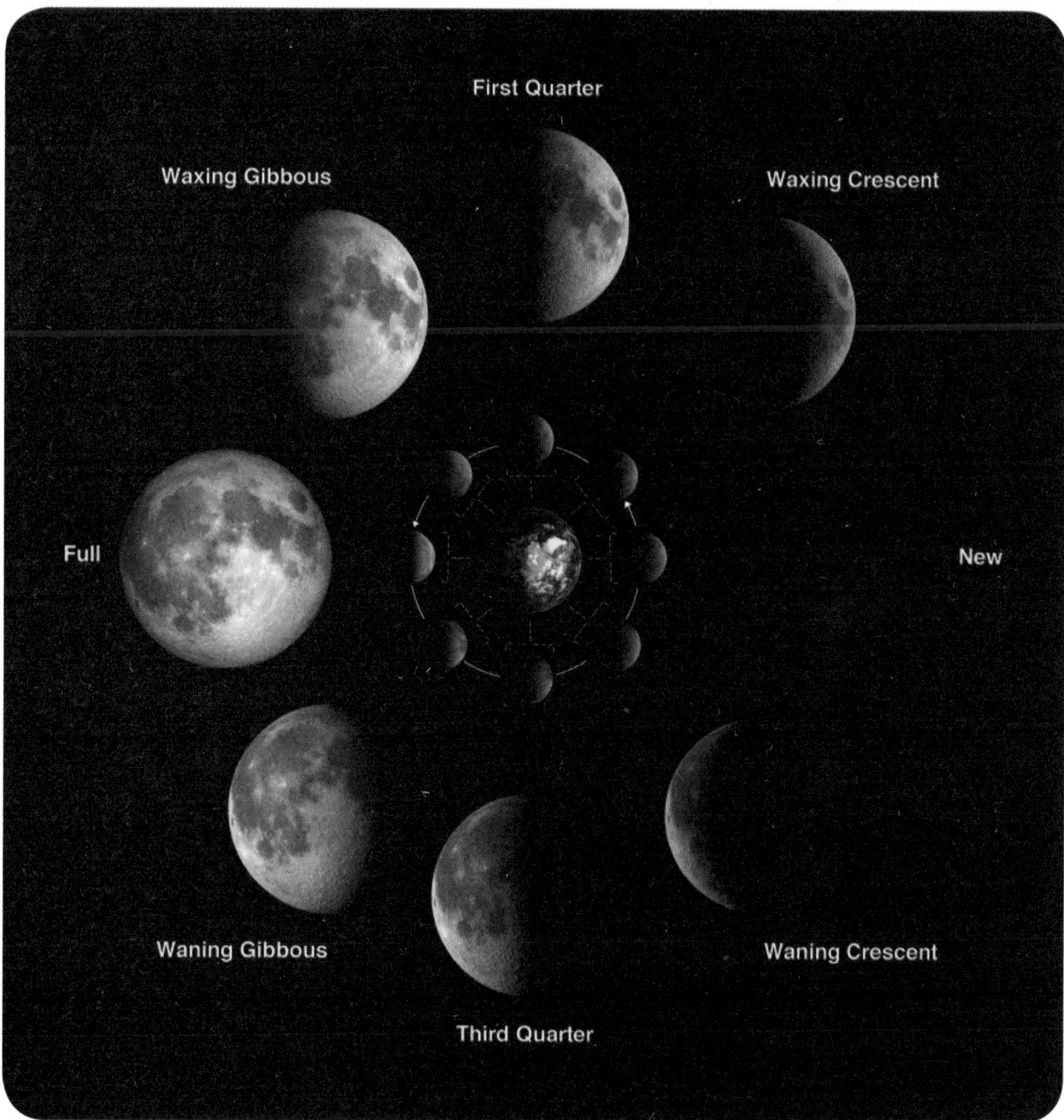

EXPLORE

Reflect

What new information did you discover on the computer?

What did this activity teach you about the moon, Earth, and the sun?

Activity 10

Analyze

Quick Code
ca8263s

The Moon's Reflection of Sunlight

Read the following text and **watch** the video. **Highlight** the sections that include evidence to support your previous answers explaining the moon phases.

EXPLORE

The Moon's Reflection of Sunlight

The moon itself does not emit its own light. It shines because its highly reflective surface, made of the light- and dark-colored rock and lunar soil, or regolith, reflects the sun's light back to Earth. Sunlight only reaches the half of the moon's surface that is facing the sun. The phase of the moon depends on its position relative to the sun and Earth.

Timing of the Moon

Activity 11

Evaluate

Quick Code
ca8264s

Explaining Moon Phases

Study the image. Using what you have learned about the phases of the moon, **write** a short paragraph explaining what the image shows and what causes the phases. **Use** the chart that follows to organize your claim, evidence, and reasons.

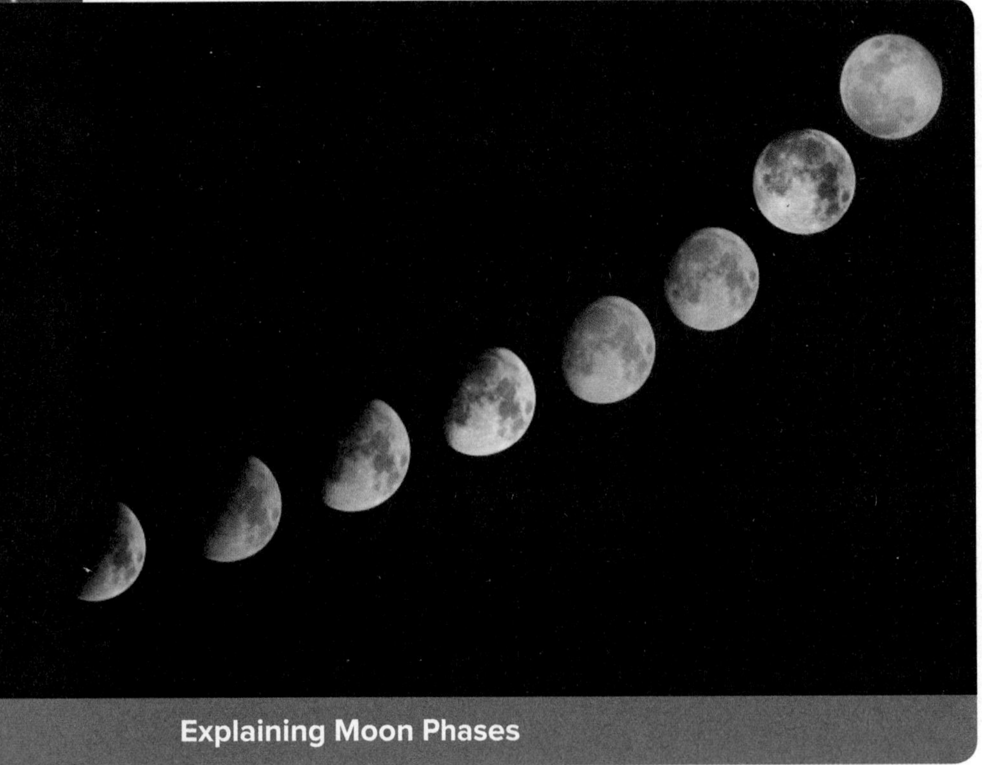

Explaining Moon Phases

CCC Patterns

Directions:

Create a scientific explanation for the question. This combines the claim that was made, the evidence that was collected, and a justification for why the evidence supports the claim (logical reasoning). The explanation should contain clear thoughts and accurate scientific vocabulary.

Claim:

Evidence

Reasoning:

How does the image communicate information in a different way from other media?

Why is this useful?

Can you suggest changes that would make this image more effective as a communications tool?

Activity 12

Reason

Modeling Eclipses

Quick Code
ca8265s

In this activity, you will model a solar and lunar eclipse.

What materials do you need? (per group)

- Foam balls, 1 in.
- Beach ball, Earth
- Lamp without a shade
- Toothpicks
- Clear light bulb

EXPLORE

Procedure

1. Form groups of three to five students.
2. Turn on your lamp and turn off the main room light.
3. Choose a type of eclipse, create its model using the large and small foam balls, and diagram with labels the arrangement of the Earth, sun, and moon. Also, sketch how the sun and/or moon would appear to an observer on Earth during the modeled eclipse.
4. Finally, model your results for the rest of the class and share your diagram. Use the chart that follows to organize your model.

SEP Developing and Using Models

CCC Systems and System Models

Before:	After:

Changes:	

Reflect

How do your diagrams of the arrangement of the Earth, sun, and moon compare with your diagrams of the appearance of the sun and/or moon from Earth?

What are some limitations of your model?

EXPLORE

Activity 13

Interpret Data

Solar Eclipse Data

Quick Code
ca8266s

Read the following passage.

Solar Eclipse Data

Solar eclipses are incredible sights: the sun is shining like a normal day, but the light seems to be slightly filtered or "off" because the moon is blocking part of the sun's light. This effect builds and builds until twilight comes in the middle of the day when the moon completely blocks the sun. The eerie sense fades as normal sunlight returns, but the experience is a worthwhile one. How can we determine when the next one will occur?

Since ancient times, humans have predicted solar and lunar eclipses. They differentiated between total eclipses, in which all the light is blocked from the sun or moon, and partial eclipses, in which only part of the light is blocked from the sun or moon. Other types of eclipses are annular eclipses and hybrid eclipses. An annular eclipse occurs when the moon is farthest from the sun and therefore cannot totally block its light. A hybrid eclipse is one that appears as a total eclipse from one location on Earth but as an annular eclipse from another location. Depending on the culture, these eclipses seemed to bring good or ill fortune. Today, we understand that such events do not foretell some divine retribution

SEP Analyzing and Interpreting Data

CCC Patterns

or favor. Rather, they are merely a function of light being blocked in the three-body system that is Earth, moon, and sun.

To predict solar eclipses, one of the tools we use is the Saros cycle. Every 18 years, 11 days, and 8 hours, which is one Saros cycle, the sun, Earth, and moon line up in the same relative geometry, which is roughly a straight line. When this occurs, a nearly identical eclipse will occur to the one that had happened one Saros cycle before. When there is a total eclipse, there will generally be another total eclipse one Saros cycle later. When there is a partial eclipse, there will generally be another partial eclipse one Saros cycle later. We say that such eclipses are in a Saros series.

EXPLORE

Now, **use** the solar eclipse data shown in the table to **answer** the questions on the following page.

Date	Eclipse type	Saros series	Date	Eclipse type	Saros series
2011 Jan 04	Partial	151	2016 Mar 09	Total	130
2011 Jun 01	Partial	118	2016 Sep 01	Annular	135
2011 Jul 01	Partial	156	2017 Feb 26	Annular	140
2011 Nov 25	Partial	123	2017 Aug 21	Total	145
2012 May 20	Annular	128	2018 Feb 15	Partial	150
2012 Nov 13	Total	133	2018 Jul 13	Partial	117
2013 May 10	Annular	138	2018 Aug 11	Partial	155
2013 Nov 03	Hybrid	143	2019 Jan 06	Partial	122
2014 Apr 29	Annular	148	2019 Jul 02	Total	127
2014 Oct 23	Partial	153	2019 Dec 26	Annular	132
2015 Mar 20	Total	120	2020 Jun 21	Annular	137
2015 Sep 13	Partial	125	2020 Dec 14	Total	142

In this data set, are any of these eclipses in the same Saros series? How do you know?

What is the relative frequency of partial eclipses in this period? What is the relative frequency of total eclipses?

If the moon and Earth had a different alignment, could that change the number of eclipses we have? Could it increase the number of eclipses? Could it decrease the number of them?

Activity 14

Evaluate

Quick Code
ca8267s

Predicting an Eclipse

Consider the data from the previous passage and table. **Use** what you know about eclipses and Saros cycles to predict a future eclipse. Using the table, **explain** how you predicted that eclipse and **describe** what type of eclipse you think it will be.

Type of Eclipse Predicted	How Did You Predict It?

SEP Engaging in Argument from Evidence

EXPLORE

What Data Do Scientists Analyze to Determine the Properties of a Planet?

Activity 15

Observe

Quick Code
ca8268s

Unknown Planet

This is a partial image of a planet in our solar system. What planet do you think it is?

Unknown Planet

Now, **look** at this full scale image and **compare** it with the previous one. What do you notice? Do you want to change your previous answer?

Unknown Planet

EXPLORE

Activity 16

Observe

Quick Code
ca8269s

Planet Images

Look at these images of different space objects. Using the table that follows, **write** quick observations about each of them. Then, **choose** one of them and **write** two or three questions about their scale properties.

Pluto

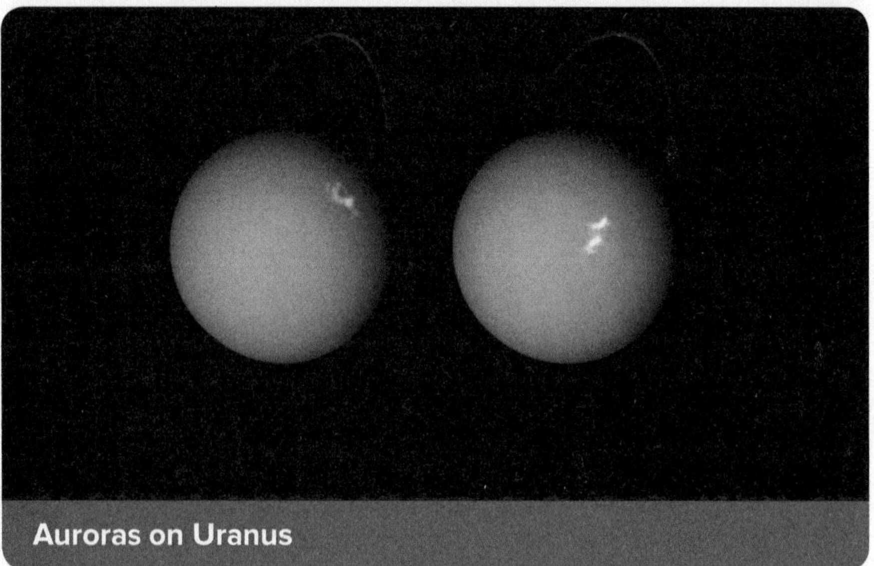

Auroras on Uranus

SEP Asking Questions and Defining Problems

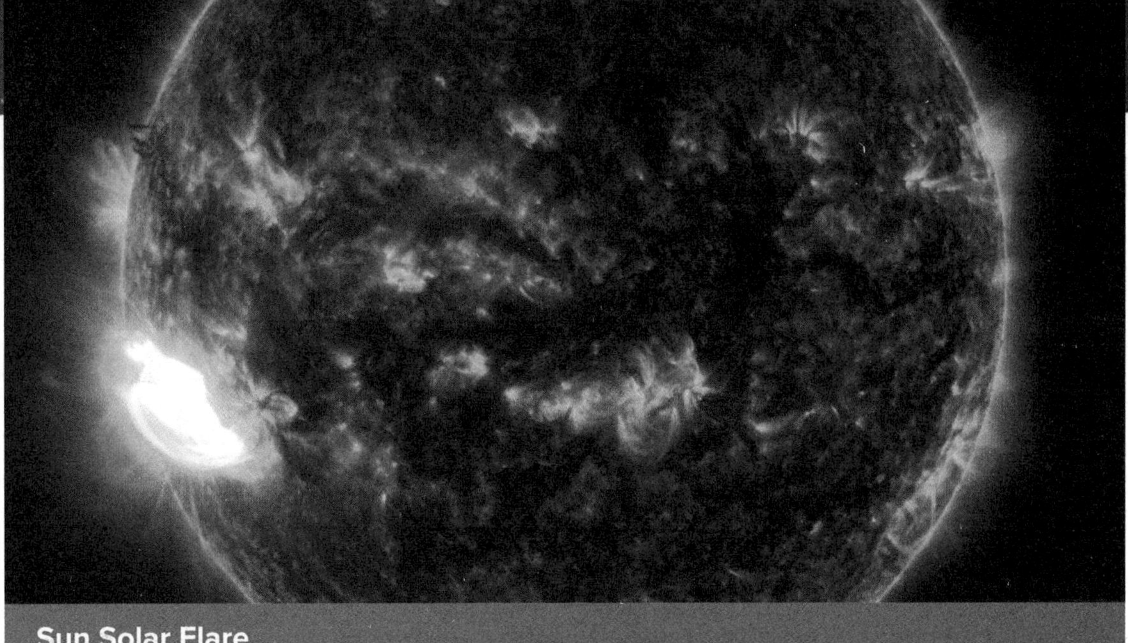

Sun Solar Flare

EXPLORE

Image	Observations	Notes/Questions
Pluto		
Auroras on Uranus		
Sun Solar Flare		

Activity 17

Observe

Quick Code
ca8270s

Scale Properties

The planets of the solar system are divided into inner and outer planets. However, within each of these two groups there are also some significant differences. **Watch** the following videos and **answer** the questions that follow.

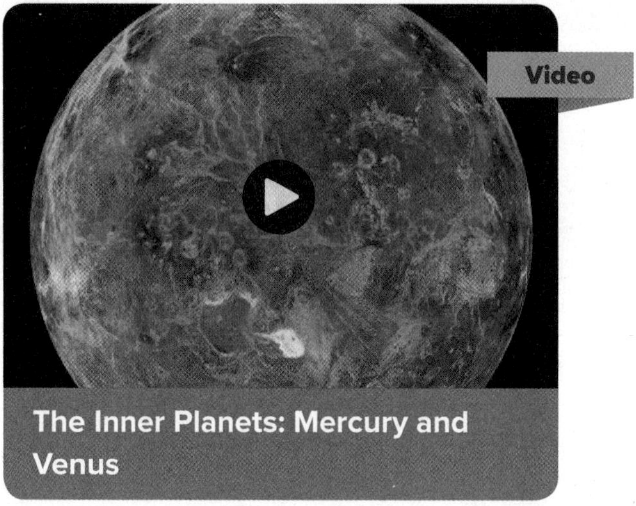

The Inner Planets: Mercury and Venus

The Outer Planets

SEP **Obtaining, Evaluating, and Communicating Information**

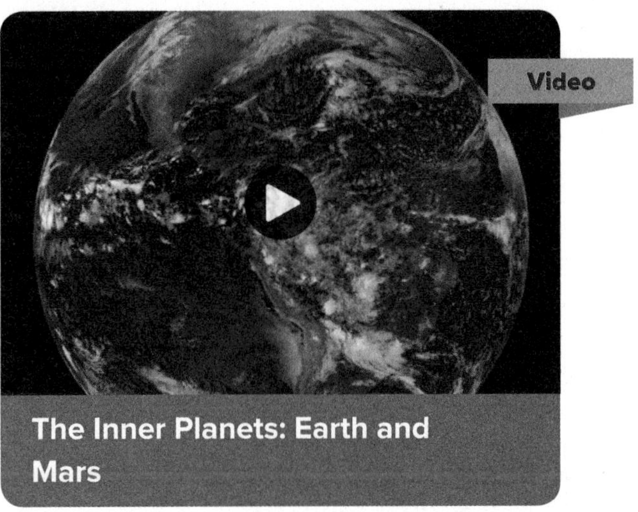

The Inner Planets: Earth and Mars

EXPLORE

Which scale properties are shared by all the inner planets?

How do the inner planets differ from one another?

Activity 18

Record Evidence

Quick Code ca8271s

Exoplanets

As you worked through this lesson, you investigated and gathered evidence about observing planetary objects. Now, take another look at the Exoplanets video, which you first saw in Engage.

How has your understanding of the video Exoplanets changed?

Read the Can You Explain? question from the beginning of this lesson.

Can You Explain?

How do we obtain data about the properties of exoplanets and objects in our solar system?

Use your new understanding of the video Exoplanets to **write** a scientific explanation answering a question.

1. **Choose** a question. You may choose to answer the Can You Explain? question, or one of the questions you wrote at the start of this lesson.
2. **Use** the following information to help you write your explanation.

You should use a scientific explanation to answer this question. Recall that a scientific explanation contains three elements: a scientific claim, evidence to support the claim, and reasoning that connects the evidence to the claim.

Use this checklist to help you plan your scientific explanation. Write your ideas in the spaces provided.

As you plan your scientific explanation, be sure to include:

- data from your investigations
- qualitative or quantitative relationships
- reliable evidence from the text
- scientific laws that apply to the real-world phenomenon
- statements indicating why the data or evidence supports your claim

Write the question you will answer here

SEP **Constructing Explanations and Designing Solutions**

EXPLAIN

Create a scientific explanation for the question. This combines the claim that was made, the evidence that was collected, and a justification for why the evidence supports the claim (logical reasoning). The explanation should contain clear thoughts and accurate scientific vocabulary.

EXPLAIN

STEM in Action

Activity 19

Analyze

Quick Code
ca8272s

Wavelengths of Light

Read this claim: Science assumes that objects and events in natural systems occur in consistent patterns that are understandable through measurement and observation.

Read the following text and **highlight** the statements that support or contradict this claim.

Wavelengths of Light

When we see an object with our telescopes, we can tell that an object is there by the **light** it reflects or gives off. From the intensity of this light, we can sometimes tell the size of the object. To some extent, we can also tell what the object is made of. The light from an object is determined in part by the materials it is made of. For example, an apple is red because it reflects red light and absorbs other wavelengths of light. Many plant leaves are green because they reflect green light and absorb other wavelengths of light.

Stars and planetary bodies are similar. They emit light of specific wavelengths because of the elements present in their bodies. For example, the **sun** is a **star** composed primarily of hydrogen, with lesser amounts of helium and even lesser amounts of oxygen, carbon, nitrogen, and a few other elements. Each element emits specific wavelengths of light determined by its atomic structure. When elements are heated, they emit these wavelengths of light. That's why you see a different color each time you burn a sample of each of these elements in a flame. The colors of light are the same as those that are emitted by these elements found deep within the sun. There, they are heated by nuclear reactions, and this intense **heat** causes these elements to emit light.

Some of the light emitted by elements deep within the sun is absorbed by other elements farther out in the cooler regions of the sun. The net effect of the combination of emission of light by interior elements and absorption by exterior elements results in an absorption/emission spectrum.

We can tell a lot about a star by the light it gives off. We can also tell a lot by the light it does not give off. In fact, some people have suggested that one way to look for intelligent life is to look for stars that have the telltale emission/absorption lines associated with uranium. This is because some civilizations might dispose of their radioactive waste into their sun. This would be visible to us when we look at the wavelengths of light emitted by that sun. Engineers, physicists, and astronomers are always designing new systems and ways to visualize different wavelengths of light. This enables them to seek out more details about planetary objects.

Wavelengths of Light *cont'd*

Christine Bland is an engineer for Lockheed Martin. She is currently working on NASA's Orion program to develop the next generation of space vehicles. She has also worked on the Spitzer Infrared Space **Telescope**, JUNO (Jupiter Orbiter), and the Mars Reconnaissance Orbiter. Bland's most significant career achievement was developing fault-management electronics. These were originally built for the Mars Reconnaissance Orbiter but have since been used on many other spacecraft. Her work allows engineers to detect, isolate, and correct malfunctions in the electronics system. Bland is also transgender. In 2011, she informed her company that she would be transitioning. Since then, she has worked to make Lockheed Martin an inclusive place. Under her leadership, they have become the first aerospace/defense company to recruit at transgender career fairs.

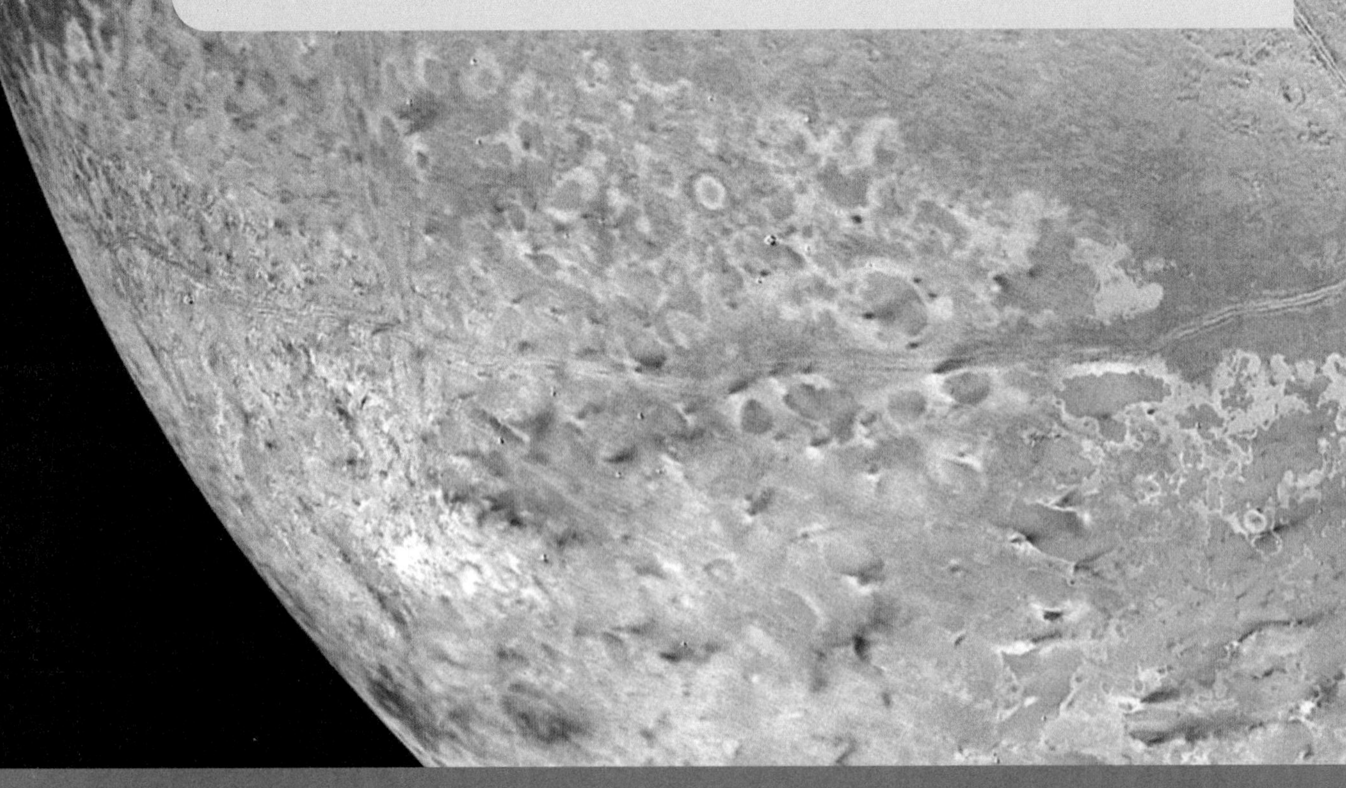

Detecting Oxygen

One of the most exciting discoveries for astrobiologists would be to discover large quantities of oxygen in the atmosphere of some planet. This is because oxygen is quite reactive. If it was not constantly replenished, oxygen would not be able to exist in an atmosphere for long. For example, consider Mars. The oxygen on Mars has reacted with the soil there, leaving none in its atmosphere. If living things were present, they might produce oxygen to replace the atmospheric oxygen that reacts with soil. Use what you know about light spectra to devise a procedure in which you use light to test for oxygen in the atmosphere of a distant planet.

Activity 20

Concept Review

Quick Code
ca8273s

Review: Observing Planetary Objects

Now that you have completed the objectives for this concept, review the core ideas you have learned. Record some of the core ideas in the space provided.

Core Ideas

Talk with a Group

Now, think about the Diamond Planet video you saw in Get Started. Discuss how what you've learned about observing planetary objects can help you understand the diamond planet.

EVALUATE

CONCEPT

2.2

Planetary Forces

Student Objectives

By the end of this lesson:

- [ ] I can develop models that describe similarities and differences in the magnetic fields around small-scale objects, such as compasses and magnets, and large-scale objects, such as planets and stars.
- [ ] I can argue from evidence that the sun has a magnetic field.
- [ ] I can collect, analyze, and interpret data to support the argument that the magnitude of magnetic and electric forces is dependent on the distance between the interacting objects.
- [ ] I can investigate the interactions of electric and magnetic forces, collect evidence to explain the cause and effect relationship between magnetic and electric forces, and predict how changes in one force affect the other.

Key Vocabulary

air, attract (magnetism), core, Earth, electric, electromagnet, equator, force, magnet, magnetic field, planet, polar, pole, repel, sun

Quick Code
ca8275s

Activity 1

Can You Explain?

How can changes in electric and magnetic forces cause water to disappear from a planet?

Quick Code
ca8276s

Activity 2

Ask Questions

Water on Mars

Quick Code
ca8277s

Read the following text and **watch** the video.

Water on Mars

Do you like watching movies and television shows about other worlds or alien life? Think of the many worlds depicted in some famous science fiction movies. It is interesting to think about life existing elsewhere in the universe. But scientists have yet to find evidence of life on other planets.

As far as we know, **Earth** is the only **planet** that supports life. Scientists study other planets that are similar to Earth. They look for signs of life. If we can find a planet with similar characteristics, there is a chance that it also could support life. Why don't other planets support life? What kinds of conditions are necessary to support life?

Let's Investigate Water on Mars

ENGAGE

Although Earth is the only planet known for sustaining life, Mars is one of the two planets in our solar system where water might have existed. Water is integral to life, so the possibility of Mars having water raised some questions. In 2012, the rover *Curiosity* landed on Mars to find some answers. Its mission was to find evidence that Mars once had water, energy, and the raw material to support life.

Like the rover *Curiosity*, you will be trying to uncover scientific evidence to support the idea that at some point life may have existed on Mars. **Write** down some questions you would like to investigate to help solve this mystery. You can pull some directly from the text, but come up with some new ones, too.

Activity 3

Evaluate

Quick Code
ca8278s

What Do You Already Know About Planetary Forces?

Distinguishing Electricity and Magnetism

Consider the properties of electric charges and magnets shown in the following list. **Write** each property beneath the appropriate description in the chart.

Properties:

- Produces a field that can apply forces to objects
- Can apply an attractive or repulsive force
- Has a north and south pole
- Is responsible for the behavior of lightning
- Can have a positive or negative charge
- Is responsible for the behavior of a compass

Properties of Electric Charge	Properties of a Magnet	Properties of Both

Analyze the Magnetic Field

Examine the drawing of a bar magnet with north and south poles as shown. At which locations does a magnetic field exist? (Note that location D is behind the magnet and location B is in front of the magnet.) Be ready to share your opinion with a partner.

Draw an X that represents a location where there is a magnetic field.

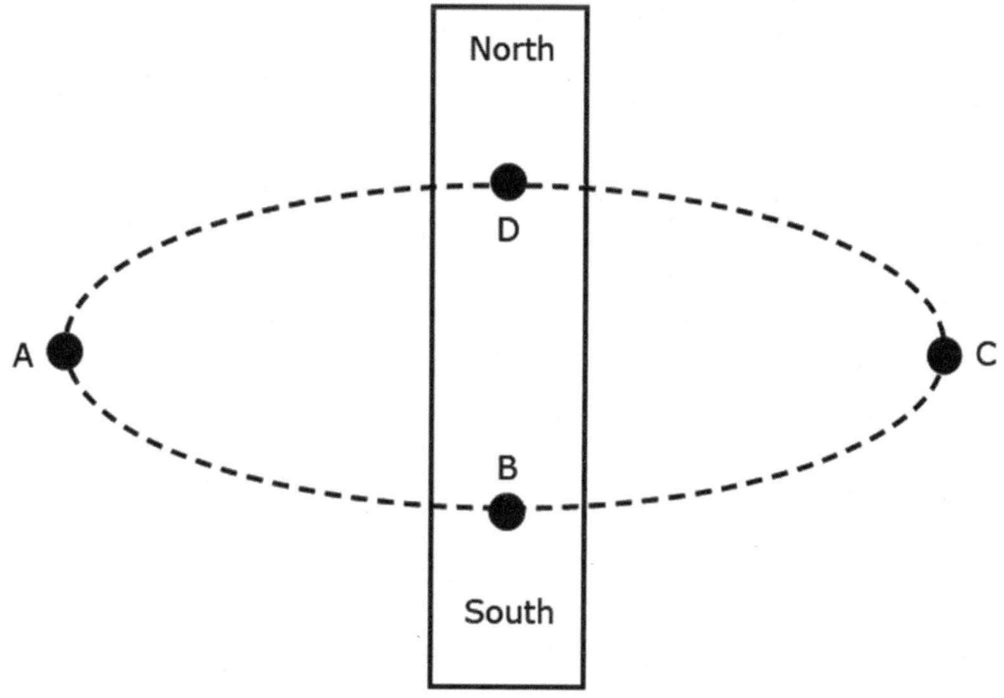

ENGAGE

Analyzing a Magnetic Field

The magnetic field of a bar magnet is shown by the arrangement of iron filings around the magnet. If steel paper clips are moved toward the bar magnet, which part or parts of the bar magnet, if any, would the paper clips be attracted to? **Draw** an X on the location or locations where the paper clips would feel the strongest attractive force. Be ready to share your thoughts with a partner.

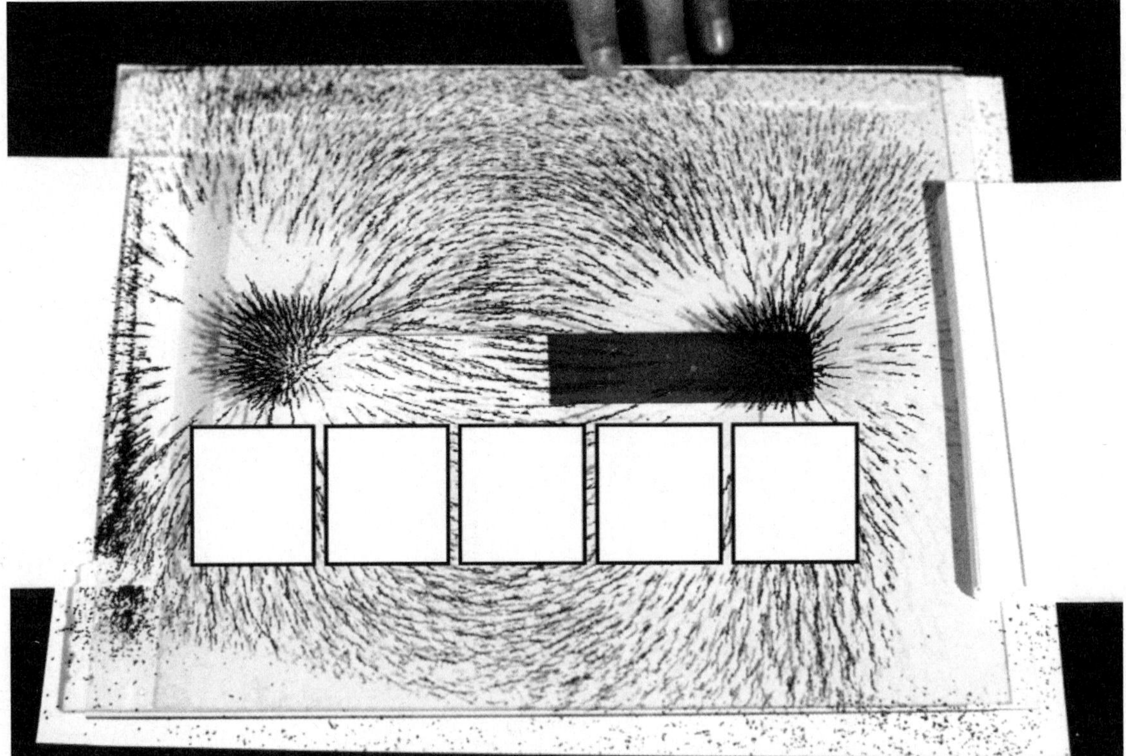

ENGAGE

Activity 4

Analyze

Quick Code
ca8279s

Magnetic Field of Earth

As you work through the concept, **use** the following chart to gather evidence to support the three claims about water on Mars.

Claim

Water is no longer found on the surface of Mars because it does not have a magnetic field.	Water is no longer found on the surface of Mars because it does not have an electric field.	Water is no longer found on the surface of Mars because of the force of gravity.

SEP **Engaging in Argument from Evidence**

SEP **Obtaining, Evaluating, and Communicating Information**

Read the following text and then **discuss** each question with three of your peers before writing your response.

EXPLORE

Magnetic Field of Earth

As the **sun** emits energy toward **Earth**, some of the radiant energy enters Earth's atmosphere and can cause evaporation of water. This is part of the water cycle. However, most of the radiant energy from the sun does not reach Earth's surface. What prevents the intense solar energy from reaching Earth's atmosphere?

Magnetic fields are produced when charged particles move. Inside the atoms of all materials, there are electrons spinning around, and they produce tiny magnetic fields around them. In regular, nonmagnetized materials, these magnetic fields spin in random directions, so they cancel each other out. But in magnetized materials, all of the electrons spin in the same direction. This means that their magnetic fields point in the same direction, and they combine to produce a larger magnetic field around the material.

What evidence do we have that Earth has a magnetic field surrounding the planet?

Can a compass provide the evidence we need?

Activity 5

Investigate

Quick Code
ca8280s

Hands-On Investigation: Detecting Magnetic Fields

In this investigation, you will use magnets, compasses, and iron filings to trace and draw magnetic fields.

EXPLORE

Predict

How do you predict the configuration (location, orientation, or number) of magnets will affect the magnetic poles and magnetic field?

CCC Cause and Effect

What materials do you need? (per group)

- White unlined paper
- Iron filings
- Compass
- Large bin, with lid
- Clear acetate sheet
- Fine tipped marker
- Colored pencils
- Masking tape
- Bar magnets
- Ring magnets
- Horseshoe magnets
- Plastic cup, 9 oz
- Lid for container for filings
- Small brushes for cleaning up stray filings (optional)

Procedure

Part 1: Finding Magnetic Poles

Gather several magnets and a colored pencil (one color). Place the magnets on a piece of paper. Trace the location and shape of the magnets. Draw several dots on the paper. Place the middle of the compass on a dot. Draw another dot to show where the north end of the compass is pointing. Label this dot N. Repeat this procedure for the rest of the dots. **Write** and **draw** your observations.

Part 2: Tracing Magnetic Fields

Make sure that the magnets from Part 1 are in their proper locations on the paper. Place another paper on top of the magnets. Tape this paper in place. From a few inches above the paper, gently sprinkle the iron filings on the top sheet of paper.

Place a bottom-side-up plastic container over the paper. Place a transparent paper over the plastic container and trace the iron filing patterns using the colored pencil you used in Part 1. **Write** and **draw** your observations in the space provided.

Part 3: Experimenting with Magnetic Fields

Repeat Parts 1 and 2 but use a different-colored pencil. For Part 1, change the location, orientation, or the number of the magnets. Be sure to use the same bottom sheet you used so you can directly compare the location, orientation, or number of the magnets. Use a different transparent sheet for each new setup in Part 2. **Write** and **draw** your observations.

Reflect

What new information did you learn about magnetic fields by experimenting with them?

How did you experiment with the new configurations of the magnets, and how did this affect the polarity (based on the compass)?

How did you experiment with the new configurations of the magnets, and how did this affect the magnetic field (based on the iron filings)?

Explain the results of your experiment. Why do you think you obtained the results that you did?

After completing the activity, review your answers to the questions you answered in Activity 4 and update them as needed:

- What evidence do we have that Earth has a magnetic field surrounding the planet?
- Can a compass provide the evidence we need?

EXPLORE

Activity 6

Analyze

Quick Code
ca8281s

Magnetic Potential Energy

Read the following text. **Underline** words or phrases that describe magnetic fields and the relationship between potential energy and the distance between two magnets. Then, **watch** the video.

Magnetic Potential Energy

A magnet is an object surrounded by a magnetic field. All magnets have a north and south pole. The magnetic field surrounding a magnet extends from the north pole and circles around the magnet to the south pole. The magnetic field describes the area around a magnet where there is a magnetic **force**. If you have ever held two bar magnets next to each other, you know that they can either push or pull each other. Just as like charges **repel** and opposite charges attract, the poles of a magnet exert attractive and repulsive forces on each other. So, if you hold the north pole of a bar magnet next to the north pole of another magnet, they will push apart. Similarly, if you hold the north pole of one magnet up to the south pole of another, the magnets will pull together. All magnets have exactly two poles.

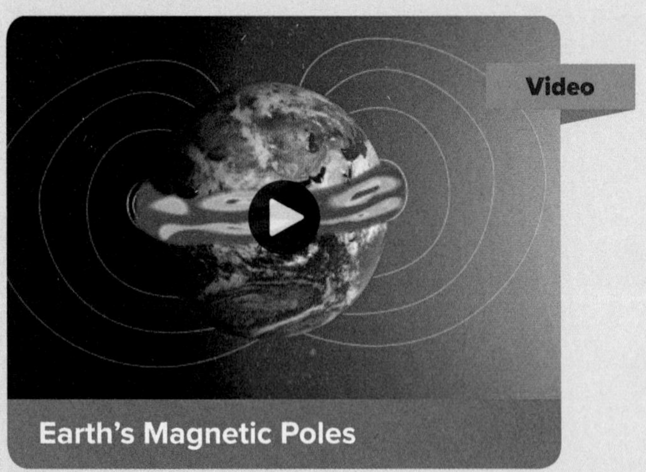

Earth's Magnetic Poles

SEP Obtaining, Evaluating, and Communicating Information

Have you ever tried to put two magnets side by side and see what happens? Two magnets separated by a distance possess potential energy. Natural magnets produce a magnetic field. This magnetic field has potential to move another magnet toward the natural magnet, if aligned to opposite poles. The greater the distance between the magnets, the greater the potential energy. Inversely, if poles are the same for the two magnets, the highest potential energy exists when the magnets are close together.

All magnets will exert a magnetic force on other magnets that are in their magnetic field. However, the strength of this force varies depending on different factors. One factor is the location in the magnetic field. The magnetic force is strongest near the poles of a bar magnet, and it is weakest near the center of the bar magnet.

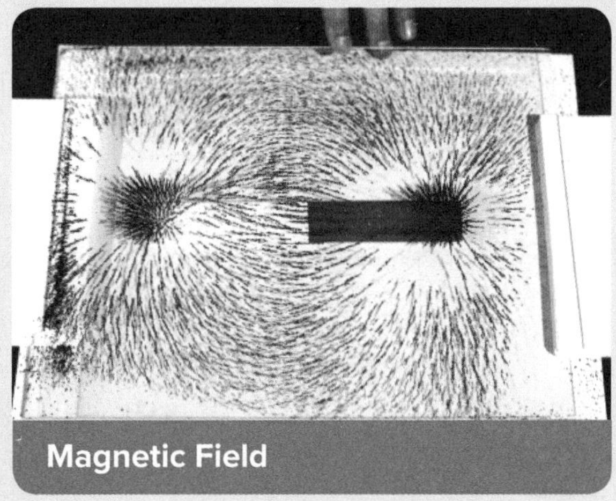

Magnetic Field

Magnetic Potential Energy *cont'd*

Similarly, the force becomes weaker as the distance from the magnet increases. Also, the magnetic field strength can depend on the size of the magnet. A small bar magnet may be able to pick up nothing heavier than a paper clip, while a very large magnet can lift a car.

With a partner, **create** a short comic strip showing the interaction of two different magnets. Be sure to include evidence from the text you have read in your comic strip. **Draw** your comic strip on a separate sheet of paper.

Activity 7

Evaluate

Quick Code
ca8282s

Investigating Magnetic Fields

Consider the following scenario, and then **complete** the activity.

A scientist is designing an experiment to investigate the relationship between the length of a bar magnet and the strength of the magnet. To measure the magnet strength, she wants to observe how many paper clips it can pick up.

Write the correct terms from the Phrase Bank into the table to show how the scientist could plan the investigation. Be prepared to share your answers with a partner and then with the class.

- Size and mass of each paper clip
- Number of paper clips
- Number of poles on the bar magnet
- Length of magnet
- Length of time magnet is held over paper clips

Investigation Component	Plan for This Investigation
Independent Variable	
Dependent Variable	
Controlled Variable	

SEP **Planning and Carrying Out Investigations**

EXPLORE

Activity 8
Analyze

Quick Code
ca8283s

Magnetic Fields of Other Planets

Read the following text and **watch** the video. **Highlight** phrases or sentences that tell you which objects in the solar system have magnetic fields.

Magnetic Fields of Other Planets

Not all planets in our solar system have a magnetosphere. Scientists use technology, such as space probes, to detect magnetic fields of other objects in our solar system, including planets. Earth has the strongest magnetic field of the rocky inner planets. The spacecraft *Mariner 10* discovered that Mercury has a weak magnetic field, while our neighbors Venus and Mars have no magnetic fields. This makes Venus and Mars more vulnerable to the radiant energy from the sun. Scientists have detected evidence of magnetic forces on specific locations on the surface of Mars, which causes scientists to question whether Mars did, at one time, have a magnetic field surrounding the planet.

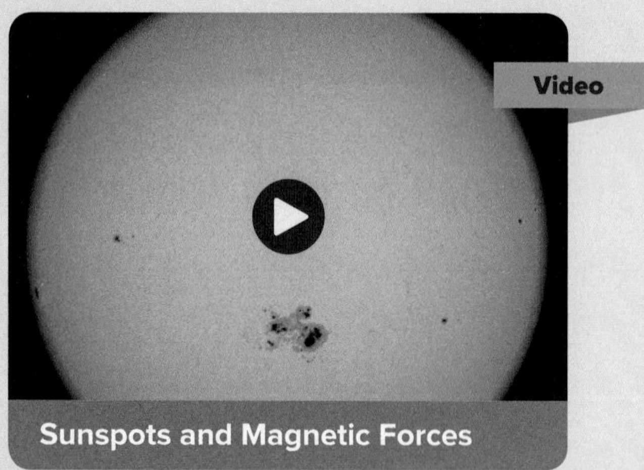

Sunspots and Magnetic Forces

Jupiter, Saturn, Uranus, and Neptune all have magnetic fields stronger than the magnetic field of Earth. Like Earth, the magnetic poles of Uranus and Neptune are not aligned to their rotation axis. Jupiter wins the strength contest by possessing a magnetic field more than 10 times greater than Earth's magnetosphere. In fact, some of Jupiter's moons have magnetic fields.

Stars, such as the sun, also emit magnetic fields. We can capture evidence of magnetic fields on the surface of the sun through images of sunspots. The sun rotates faster at its **equator** than it does at its poles. This causes its magnetic field to twist, forming sunspots. Sunspots are dark, intense magnetic fields that appear on the photosphere of the sun. Because sunspots are magnetic fields, they always appear in pairs. The sun's powerful magnetic field causes solar storms, which can include solar flares (jets of hot gases that explode off the sun) and prominences (loops of gas ejected off the sun).

EXPLORE

Using the information from the text and video, **create** three true statements and one false statement. After you write your statements in the space provided, **share** your statements with a classmate to guess which statement is false.

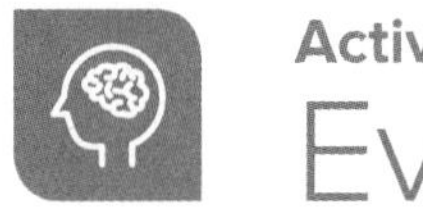

Activity 9

Evaluate

Quick Code
ca8284s

Magnetic Interactions

The model shows the interaction between two magnetic fields. One of these fields is exerted by the sun via the solar wind (yellow lines). The other is exerted by Earth (green lines).

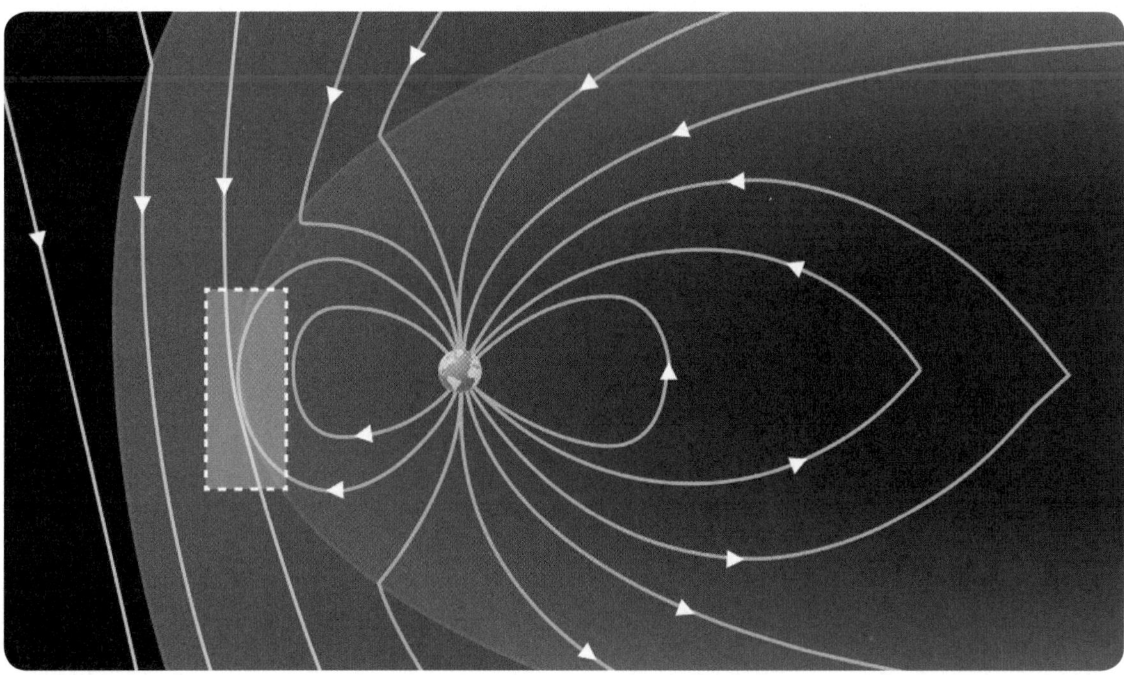

Describe the relationship between the sun's magnetic field and Earth's magnetic field.

CCC **Systems and System Models**

EXPLORE

Now, **think** about a compass. A compass is part of another system of interacting magnetic fields. **Describe** how a compass works.

Draw the magnetic field line of a compass.

Explain which magnetic fields interact to allow a compass to work and how a model of these interactions is similar to and different from the model of the sun's and Earth's magnetic fields.

Activity 10
Analyze

Quick Code
ca8285s

Electrical Force

Take a look at the image. The lines represent the electric forces between two oppositely charged particles.

Electric Force Lines

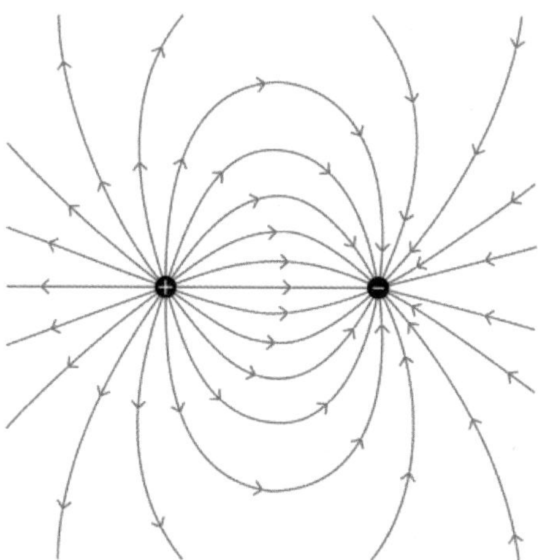

As you read the following text, **look** for the answers to the following questions:

- How do these electric force lines compare with the magnetic field lines around Earth?
- What happens to the electric potential energy if the distance between the particles increases?

Electrical Force

On **Earth**, we find materials that are naturally magnetic. An example is the mineral called lodestone. In lodestone, all the electrons naturally spin in the same direction, so the mineral produces a **magnetic field** around it. Lodestone was one of the first magnets used in early compasses. Some metallic objects near a magnetic object will be drawn to it, while others will not be affected. Some objects are even pushed away from one end of a magnetic object.

The magnetic field of Earth is not the combination of the magnetic fields of all these naturally magnetic materials. The magnetic field of Earth is the result of another **noncontact force**, an electrical force. An electrical force is what holds atoms together.

All matter can be electrically charged. For example, electrons surrounding the nucleus of an atom are negatively charged. Protons in the nucleus are positively charged. All **electric** charges exert forces on each other. Like magnetic forces, electrical forces act according to the following principle: Like charges **repel** and opposites **attract**. This means that when two of the same charges, such as two protons (positive charges) come near each other, they will each experience a force pushing each away from the other one. Similarly, when two opposite charges—such as a negative and positive charge—come near each other they experience a force pulling them together.

EXPLORE

Electrical potential energy is stored when you do work against an electrical force. For example, in a battery, it takes work to separate positive and negative charges because they are attracted to each other. Chemical reactions inside of a battery do this, so there are positive charges at one terminal and negative charges at another. This separation of charges stores electrical potential energy in the battery. When a wire is connected to the terminals in a battery, negative charges flow through the wire from the negative terminal to the positive terminal, just as a skier slides from the top of a mountain to the bottom. The electrical potential energy for a charged particle is related to the distances between the charges.

The area surrounding a charged particle is known as an electric field, and it can be thought of as a force field. If a charge moves into an electric field, it will be attracted or repelled, depending on its charge. Like the poles of a **magnet**, the electrical field is strongest near the source of the charge. The electrical field becomes weaker at greater distances from the source of the charge.

How do these electric force lines compare with the magnetic field lines around Earth?

What happens to the electrical potential energy if the distance between the particles increases?

Activity 11

Evaluate

Quick Code
ca8286s

Ranking Electrostatic Forces

Study the table that describes pairs of charged particles. Then, **use** the information to **fill in** the diagram that follows, ranking the pairs by electrostatic force.

	Particle 1 Charge	Particle 2 Charge	Distance between Particles (Picometers)
Pair 1	+1	–1	0.5
Pair 2	–1	–1	0.2
Pair 3	+1	+1	0.8
Pair 4	–1	+1	0.3

Fill in the diagram with the numbered tiles to rank the pairs in order from the pair experiencing the smallest electrostatic force to the pair experiencing the largest electrostatic force. (A picometer is a trillionth of a meter.)

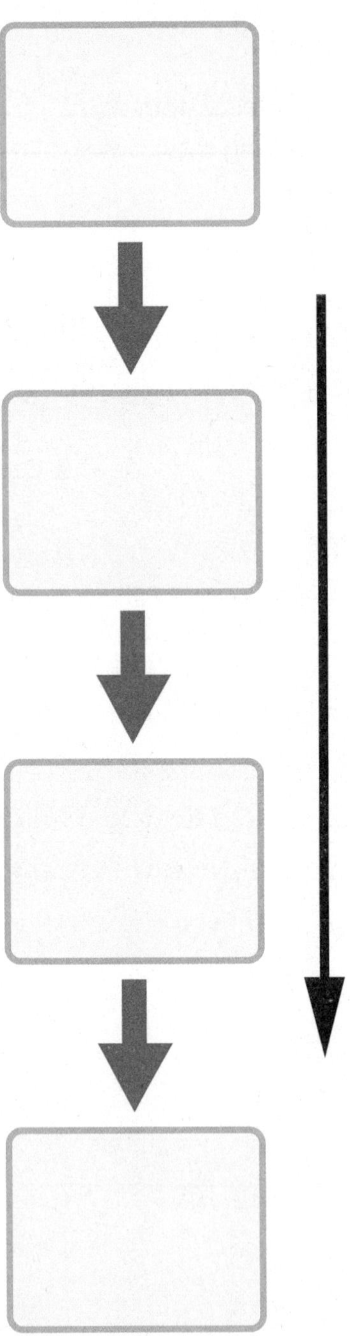

Increasing electrostatic force between particles

Activity 12

Observe

Electricity

Quick Code
ca8287s

Read the following passage. Then, you will **go online** to explore the relationship between electricity and magnetism.

EXPLORE

In 1831, Michael Faraday discovered that a changing magnetic field could generate an electric current in a wire. This can be accomplished by moving a magnet perpendicular to a wire. The relative motion between the magnet and the wire creates voltage across the wire. The movement of the magnet in and out of the coil causes the current to alternate. Faraday built the first electric generator that converted the back-and-forth motion of a magnet in and out of a wire coil into electric energy. He soon learned that moving the coil of wire while the magnet stood still produced the same current. He built an apparatus called the Faraday disk that used a spinning copper disk in a horseshoe magnet that proved his theory. The electric circuit was completed by stationary wires, called brushes, that touched the disk on its rim and on its axle.

Faraday later theorized that the voltage in a coil of wire is proportional to the product of the number of coils and the rate at which the magnetic field changes in those coils. This is now called Faraday's law.

SEP **Planning and Carrying Out Investigations**

CCC **Scale, Proportion, and Quantity**

After that, the search was on to invent an efficient generator capable of producing a constant electric current. In 1832, Hippolyte Pixii built an electric generator that converted the rotary movement of a magnet into electrical energy. By 1850, a high-current generator had been built in France, and in 1877 in Germany, Seimens invented a "dynamo." Edison adapted the dynamo to light up New York City in 1882. In 1887, the patent for Nikola Tesla's AC generator was bought by Westinghouse and usable electricity spread across the United States.

Follow the procedure listed as you work through the interactive. Then, answer the questions that follow.

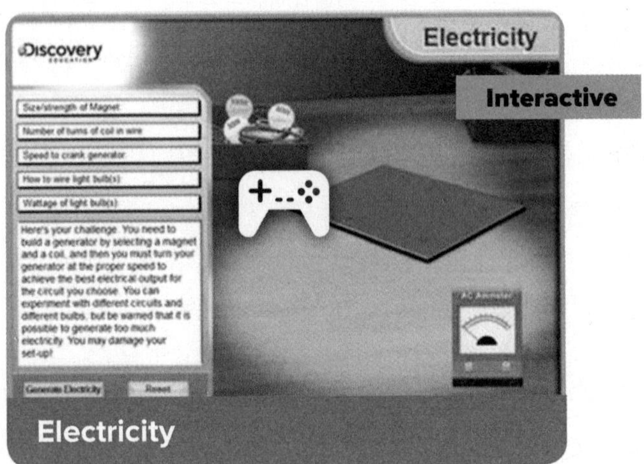

Procedure

1. **Click** on the Start Here button and **read** the text. If you need more information, click and read the Background. **Close** the window when you are done.
2. Now, **set up** the generator that you will test. Under Strength of Magnet, **select** Small. Under Number of Turns of Coil in Wire, **select** Few.

3. **Start** by selecting the circuit that you will test. From the pull-down menu under Wattage of Light Bulb, **select** 100-watt bulb. Under How to Wire the Light Bulb, **select** 1 Bulb.

4. There are three variables under Speed to Crank Generator. **Start** with Slow.

5. **Click** on the Start Generator button. **Record** the results in the first row of the table.

Ammeter Reading of Generator			
	Speed of Crank		
Number of Coils	Slow	Medium	Fast
Few			
More			
Many			

6. **Repeat** this for the remaining two options under Speed to Crank Generator. **Record** the results of each in the remaining spaces in the first row for a few turns.

7. Next, under Number of Turns of Coil in Wire, **select** More. **Repeat** steps 5–7, recording results in the second row of the table.

8. Finally, under Number of Turns of Coil in Wire, **select** Many. Again, **repeat** steps 5–7, recording results in the third row.

The maximum current in a circuit is directly related to the watts in the light bulb. A light bulb will never “pull” more current than is needed for it to light. However, the circuit has a maximum current available. At which combinations of speed and coils for a generator did the circuit reach its maximum? How could you tell?

Look carefully at the changes in the ammeter readings. **Describe** the pattern in the progression of numbers.

Across the rows:

Down the columns:

Faraday's law states that the induced voltage in a coil is proportional to the product of the number of loops and the rate at which the magnetic field changes within those loops. **Use** the patterns you observed to develop an explanation for how Faraday's law applies to three generators that you tested.

Activity 13

Analyze

Electricity and Magnetism Relationship

Quick Code
ca8288s

Read the following text, and then **answer** the question.

Electricity and Magnetism Relationship

An electric current is the movement of charged particles through a conducting wire. When an electric current flows through a wire, a magnetic field is produced around the wire. If the wire is wrapped around a metal **core**, the magnetic field produced by the flowing current is strengthened.

We can take advantage of this effect to build **electromagnets**. A simple electromagnet is a wire wrapped around a metal core that is connected to a power source. When electricity flows through the wire, a magnetic field is generated. This is useful because it allows operators to turn the magnet off or on by turning the power off or on. An electromagnet can be made more powerful by increasing the number of times the wire is coiled around the metal core or by increasing the current of the electricity source. The extra electrons flowing around the electromagnet strengthen the magnetic field.

Electricity and magnetism are also related in that magnets can be used to generate electricity. This process works like the reverse of an electromagnet. Moving a wire through a magnetic field causes an electric current to flow in the wire. This is called electromagnetic induction. Electromagnetic induction is how electric generators work.

Which pieces of data from the Interactive "Electricity" you completed earlier support two statements within the text?

Activity 14
Analyze

Quick Code
ca8289s

Earth as a Generator

Read the text and **watch** the video.

EXPLORE

Earth as a Generator

Earth's magnetic field is the result of the convective motion of Earth's liquid metal in the outer core. Earth's structure includes an inner core, outer core, mantle, and crust.

The center of Earth is called the core. It is divided into the outer core and inner core. The outer core is made of liquid iron and nickel. During the formation of Earth, these elements were very heavy and sank to the interior of the **planet**. The intense heat and pressure cause the outer core to be liquid. The inner core is solid iron and nickel. The temperature of both the inner and outer cores are estimated to be 5,000–6,000°C. The reason for the difference in phase is the intense pressure.

Earth's Core Electrical Forces

SEP **Obtaining, Evaluating, and Communicating Information**

Even with similar temperatures, the inner core is solid because it is under more pressure. The outer molten core spins around the solid inner core. Circulating electrical currents through Earth's interior originating in the metallic outer core generate a magnetic field around Earth.

Our knowledge about Earth can help us predict why Mars does not have a magnetic field. The core of Mars cooled and solidified, so it does not have a liquid outer core like Earth. As such, there is no convection of liquid metal to generate a strong magnetic field to protect the Martian atmosphere. As a result, Mars has a very thin atmosphere that does little to regulate its temperature. The average temperature of the Martian surface is –65°C. This keeps the water frozen in thick **polar** ice caps most of the time, though evidence suggests this was not always the case.

In groups, **complete** the Venn diagram to identify two similarities and two differences between the generator you tested in the Interactive "Electricity" and the passage Earth as a Generator.

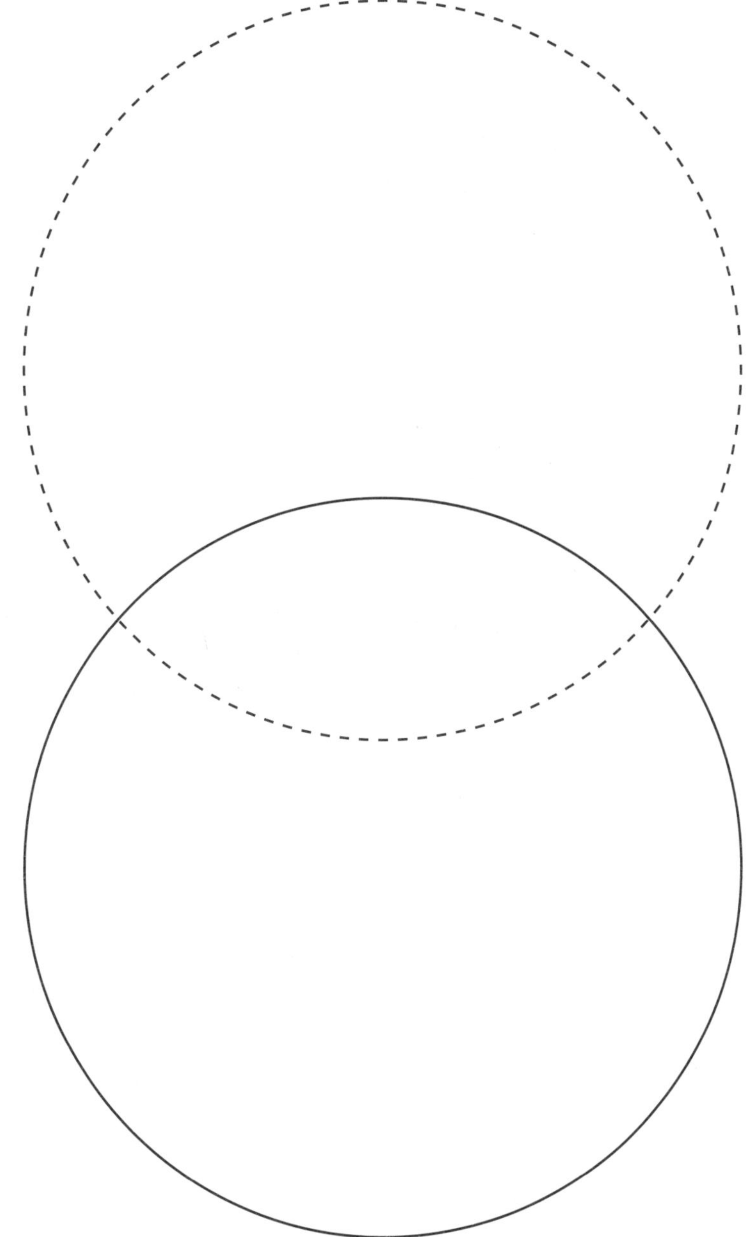

EXPLORE

Activity 15

Record Evidence

Quick Code
ca8290s

Water on Mars

As you worked through this lesson, you investigated and gathered evidence about planetary forces. Now, take another look at the video Water on Mars, which you first saw in Engage.

How has your understanding of the Water on Mars video changed?

Read the Can You Explain? question from the beginning of this lesson.

Can You Explain?

How can changes in electric and magnetic forces cause water to disappear from a planet?

Recall the claims provided to you at the beginning of Explore:

1. Water is no longer found on the surface of Mars because it does not have a magnetic field.
2. Water is no longer found on the surface of Mars because it does not have an electric field.

3. Water is no longer found on the surface of Mars because of the force of gravity.

Select one of the claim statements to create your scientific explanation. Then, use this checklist to help you plan your scientific explanation. Write your ideas in the spaces provided.

As you plan your scientific explanation, be sure to include:

- data from your investigations
- qualitative or quantitative relationships
- reliable evidence from the text
- scientific laws that apply to the real-world phenomenon
- statements indicating why the data or evidence supports your claim

Write the Claim You Selected

SEP **Constructing Explanations and Designing Solutions**

EXPLAIN

Create a scientific explanation for the question. This combines the claim that was made, the evidence that was collected, and a justification for why the evidence supports the claim (logical reasoning). The explanation should contain clear thoughts and accurate scientific vocabulary.

EXPLAIN

STEM in Action

Activity 16

Analyze

Quick Code
ca8291s

Solar Storm Chasers

Read the text and **watch** the videos. **Underline** key details in the text and **take notes** as you watch the videos.

Solar Storm Chasers

When bad weather strikes, communication is key to getting help to people who need it. But what if that weather can knock out communications systems? Scientists at the National Space Weather Center monitor changes in the solar wind so they can send out a warning when trouble is heading our way.

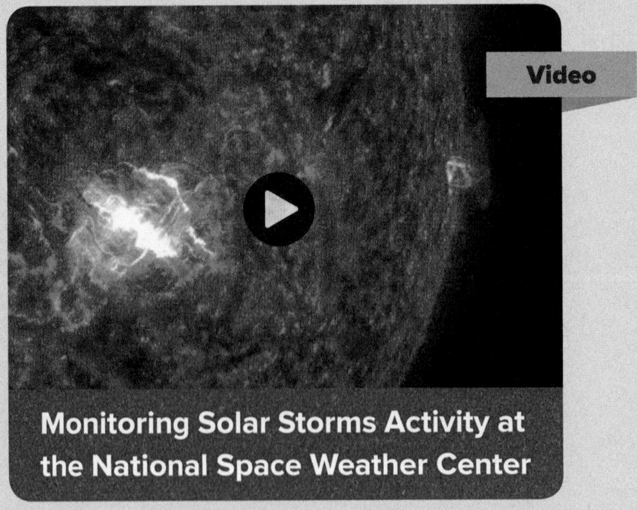

Monitoring Solar Storms Activity at the National Space Weather Center

The corona is the outermost layer of the **sun**'s atmosphere. It normally is visible only during a solar eclipse, when the moon blocks the disk of the sun. When huge amounts of mass are ejected, or blasted away, from the sun's corona, we can expect some problems.

Disruption from Solar Storms

The solar wind slamming against **Earth's magnetic field** can shut off lights. However, it also can turn up the lights in some parts of the world.

Preparing for the Future

ELABORATE

Matching Cause and Effect

Weathercasters watch for changes in the solar wind. Solar wind affects different systems on Earth in different ways. **Draw** a line from each effect of solar wind on Earth to its cause.

Cause	Effect
Electrons follow magnetic field lines and collide with molecules of gas in the atmosphere.	Loss of power
Changing magnetic fields generate electricity in wires.	Loss of communication
The upper layer of the atmosphere is heated and expands.	Increase in aurorae

Explain your reasoning for each match. **Use** evidence from the text to support your explanation. Be prepared to compare answers and reasoning with a partner.

ELABORATE

Activity 17

Concept Review

Quick Code
ca8292s

Review: Planetary Forces

Now that you have completed the objectives for this concept, review the core ideas you have learned. Record some of the core ideas below.

Core Ideas

EVALUATE

Talk with a Group

Now, think about the Diamond Planet video you saw in Get Started. Discuss how what you've learned about planetary forces can help you understand the diamond planet.

Orbital Forces

Student Objectives

By the end of this lesson:

- [ ] I can argue from evidence that the force of gravity is dependent on the masses of the interacting objects as well as their distance from each other.
- [ ] I can develop models of the force of gravity that describe and predict the motion of small-scale objects on the surface of Earth and large-scale objects such as orbiting planets.
- [ ] I can model the force of gravity and inertia to simulate orbits of planets around the sun.
- [ ] I can construct an explanation of the role of gravity in the formation of the solar system.
- [ ] I can obtain, evaluate, and communicate information about how technology enhances our ability to understand the solar system and make predictions about solar system objects.

Key Vocabulary

asteroid, axis, comet, core, diameter, Earth, gravity, Kuiper Belt, latitude, moon, orbit, position, revolution, rotate, rotation, space, star, sun, surface, system, theory

Quick Code
ca8294s

Activity 1

Can You Explain?

How does the force of gravity move objects in the solar system?

Quick Code
ca8295s

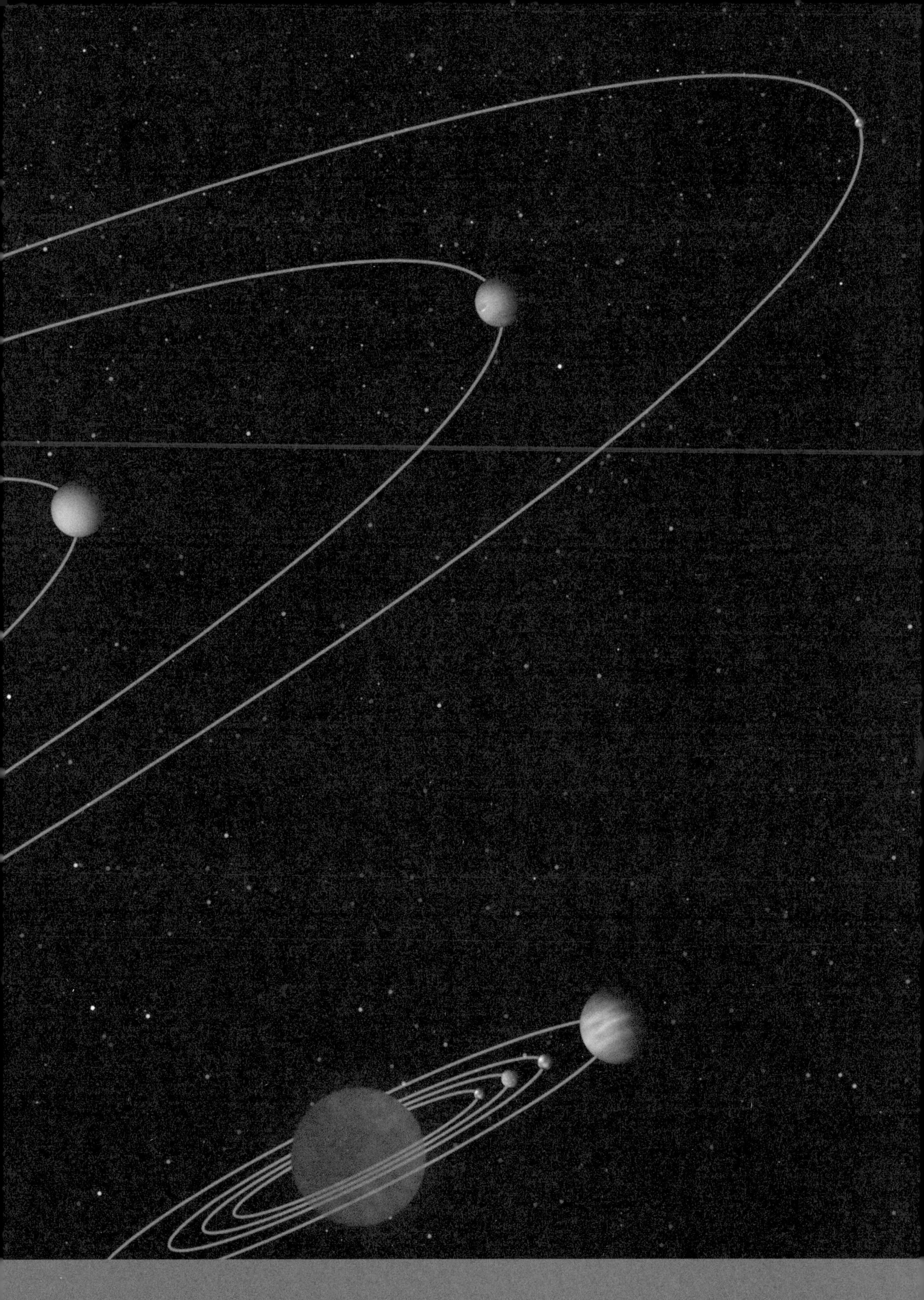

Activity 2
Ask Questions

Quick Code
ca8296s

Pluto's Moons

Watch this video, and **answer** the questions that follow.

Video

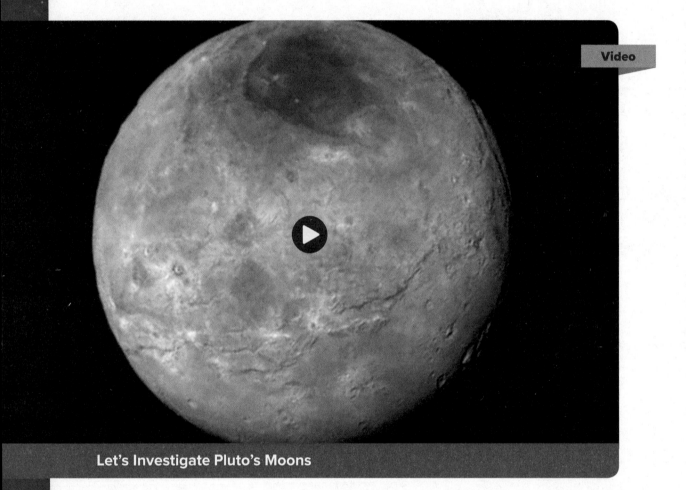

Let's Investigate Pluto's Moons

What do you already know about Pluto?

What are the criteria scientists use to classify a planet?

What questions do you have about Pluto, its moons, or what makes something a planet?

Activity 3

Analyze

Quick Code
ca8297s

Pluto

Read the text and **watch** the videos. As you read and view the videos, **use** the T-Chart to **capture** information about what you already know and what you know now.

Pluto

Why is Pluto no longer considered a planet? Pluto, now renamed Object 134-340, originally was identified as a planet in our solar **system** in 1930. Pluto is found even farther out in **space** than Neptune, at 39.48 astronomical units away from the **sun**, and it has an **orbit** path that is oval. One year on Pluto is almost 248 **Earth** years, and one day on Pluto is equivalent to 6.39 Earth days. Because its **surface** is made primarily of frozen nitrogen, it has a density that is 38 percent that of Earth's density. Scientists believe that the **core** of Pluto is quite large and rocky. Pluto has a very low mass relative to Earth's (0.00218 Earths), and it is approximately 19 percent of Earth's **diameter**. Pluto has several moons, including one very large **moon** called Charon. Charon is almost half of Pluto's size.

Pluto's Moons

ENGAGE

Pluto was classified as a planet until 2006, when the International Astronomical Union (IAU) redefined the qualifications of a planet. This reclassification came after scientists discovered an object that was bigger than Pluto, called Eris. Scientists had already been debating whether Pluto should be a planet because other objects had been found nearby that were similar in size to it. Finding Eris was the tipping point that caused the removal of Pluto's status as a planet.

Pluto: A Dwarf Planet

The IAU states that to be classified as a planet, in our solar system, the object must:

- Orbit the sun
- Have enough mass for **gravity** to form it into a sphere
- Have enough mass that it does not interact with objects within its orbit

Unfortunately for Pluto, other objects were found within its orbital path; therefore, it was reclassified as a dwarf planet.

Pluto and Charon

Use the T-Chart to capture connections between what you already knew about Pluto and what you know now.

Topic:____

What I Already Knew	What I Know Now

ENGAGE

Activity 4

Evaluate

Quick Code ca8298s

What Do You Already Know About Orbital Forces?

What Do You Know?

Which statements correctly describe galaxies in the universe? **Select** all that apply.

- ☐ There are different types of galaxies.
- ☐ Once formed, a galaxy stays the same shape and size.
- ☐ Galaxies are affected by gravity.
- ☐ All galaxies contain billions of stars.
- ☐ Our planet, but not our sun, is within our galaxy.
- ☐ There are more stars than galaxies.

Thinking About Gravity

Answer the question in the space provided.

What role did gravity play in the formation of the solar system?

ENGAGE

Gravitational Effect

The model represents the orbit of a planet around a star. The planet traveling the orbit is traveling counterclockwise.

Draw a solid arrow in the correct location that shows the direction of the force of gravity acting on the motion of the planet.

Draw a dashed arrow that shows the direction of the planet's sideways motion.

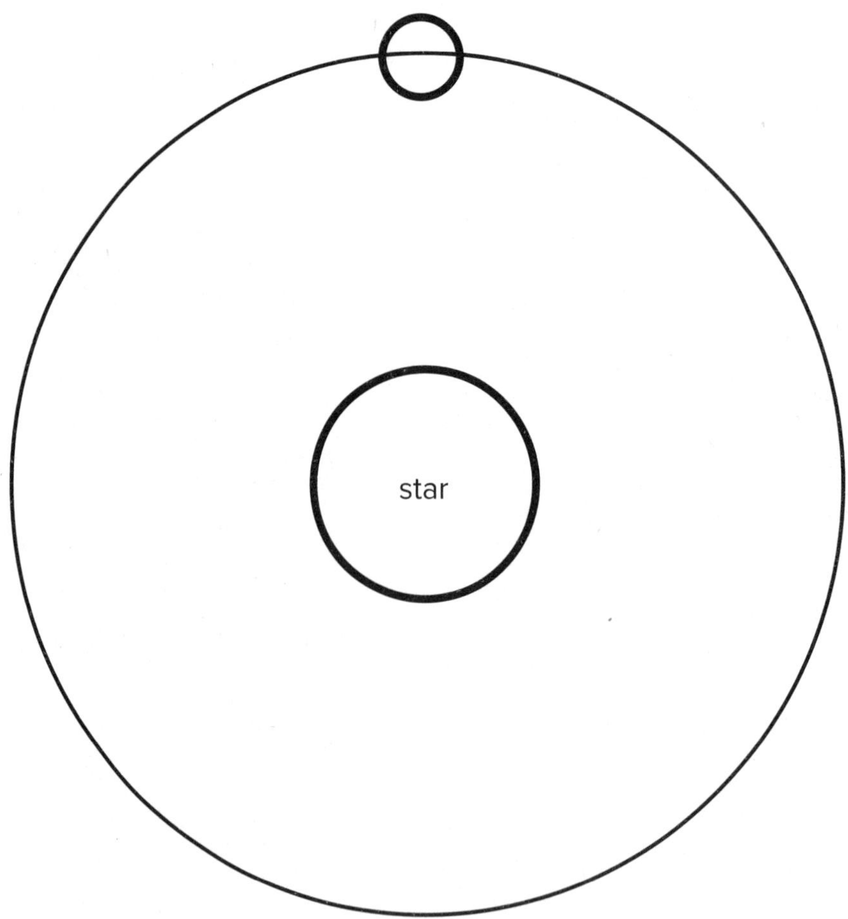

ENGAGE

What Role Did Gravity Play in the Formation of the Solar System?

Activity 5

Analyze

Quick Code
ca8299s

Gravity's Role in Formation of Solar System Objects

Read the following text about gravity. As you read, **underline** the central ideas and details about the formation of solar system objects.

Gravity's Role in Formation of Solar System Objects

You already learned that electric and magnetic noncontact forces exist in our solar **system**. **Gravity**, another noncontact force, was central to the development of the solar system. Gravity is the force of attraction that occurs between masses and draws objects toward each other. The strength of an object's gravitational pull on another object is controlled by the mass of each object and the distance between them. The greater the masses and the shorter the distance, the greater is the gravitational pull between objects.

Scientists think that the solar system formed in a process that is described by the nebular **theory**. According to the nebular theory, the solar system began to form about 4.6 billion years ago from a giant rotating cloud of gas and dust called a solar nebula.

An unknown event, such as the shockwave caused by a supernova or the movement of a passing **star**, caused the cloud to begin to collapse under its own gravity, and the giant gas cloud began to contract.

Formation of the Sun

It was the force of gravity that caused the material in the nebula to move toward the center in the first place. As the gas cloud collapsed, it took the shape of a flat disk of gas and dust, rotating faster and faster as it contracted.

As material moved toward the center of the disk, the gravitational pull of the center increased, pulling in even more material. About 99.8 percent of all the material eventually formed a giant ball of gas and dust at the center of the disk. The pressure created by accumulating matter forced the material to heat up. The extremely high pressure and temperature at the center of the disk caused hydrogen atoms to fuse together to form helium. This reaction began to give off tremendous amounts of energy, and the ball of material began to glow. By about 4.56 billion years ago, the star we call the **sun** had formed.

EXPLORE

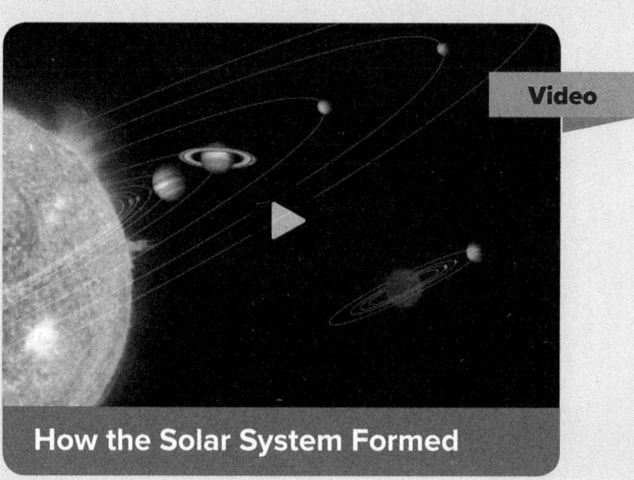

How the Solar System Formed

Formation of the Planets

Although most of the material that was originally in the nebula collapsed to form the sun, there was still plenty left. This material continued to revolve around the center.

Over time, it also came together under the force of gravity. Small rocks came together to form large rocks. Large rocks came together to form planetesimals, and planetesimals collided to form planets. Other clumps of material formed smaller objects such as the dwarf planets, moons, asteroids, and comets. This process is known as accretion.

Gravity continues to build the planets. Scientists estimate that gravity causes roughly 60 tons of dust to be pulled to **Earth** each day. Gravity causes rocks from **space** to strike Earth and other planets and moons on a daily basis and, on occasion, gravity also brings an **asteroid** or **comet** on a collision course with a planet.

Use the storyboard graphic organizer to plan a comic strip depicting the significant events beginning with a nebula and continuing to the current configuration of planets orbiting the sun.

Complete the map that follows to help you plan your comic strip story.

EXPLORE

Create your comic strip in the space provided.

How Does the Force of Gravity Keep a Planet in Orbit?

Activity 6

Observe

Quick Code
ca8301s

EXPLORE

Gravity and Planetary Motion

After watching the video, you will demonstrate the force of gravity that acts on planets in orbit. Following the demonstration, answer the questions.

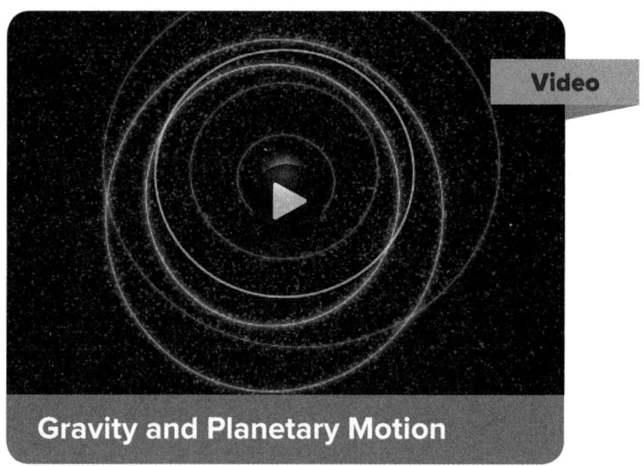

Gravity and Planetary Motion

What force was eliminated in the demonstration?

How does the demonstration simulate the behavior of satellites?

What happens if the person in the middle is stronger than the person on the other end of the rope?

Activity 7

Evaluate

Quick Code
ca8300s

Birth of a Solar System

Use your knowledge of the creation of the sun to **circle** the correct words to complete the paragraph.

About 4.6 billion years ago, the solar system started as a giant cloud of gas and dust called [**nuclear fusion/a solar nebula/the shockwave/a supernova**]. Some event, such as [**a supernova/the creation of a planet/the formation of the sun/a black hole**], caused a [**fusion/orbital/metallic/gravitational**] collapse at the center of the cloud. Most of the dust and gas in the cloud collapsed on itself. It formed a [**supernova/elliptical orbit/spinning disk/spiral galaxy**] of gas and dust. The heat of this collapse caused [**shockwave/supernova/fusion/fission**] to occur, resulting in the development of the sun.

EXPLORE

Activity 8
Analyze

The Role of Gravity

Quick Code
ca8302s

Read the following text about the the role of gravity.

The Role of Gravity

In your investigations of how the force of **gravity** pulls objects toward **Earth's surface**, did you consider that the force of gravity is present outside of Earth's atmosphere? If gravity is a powerful enough force to pull together dust and gas to create stars and planets, what else can gravity do?

Sir Isaac Newton discovered that the same force that causes apples to fall from a tree, gravity, can be used to explain patterns of motion in our solar **system** and across galaxies. Johannes Kepler expanded our understanding of the impact of gravity by observing and describing patterns of motion in the solar system.

The strength of a gravitational force varies directly with the masses of the objects and inversely with the square of the distance between them. This means that the closer and more massive an object is, the more gravity that object will be able to exert. Earth is the most massive object in its region of **space**.

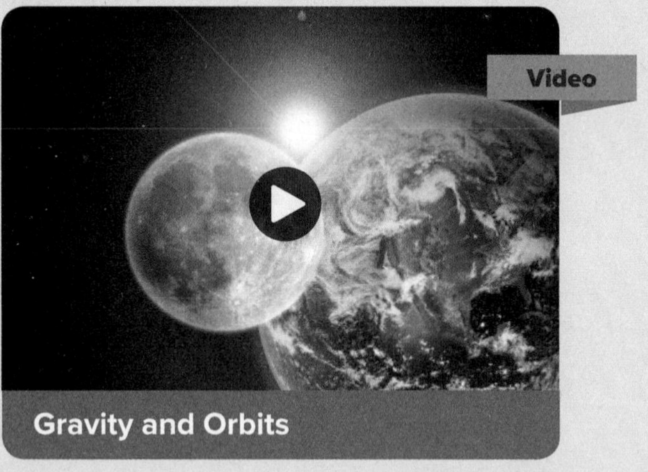

Gravity and Orbits

CCC Cause and Effect

EXPLORE

The gravity of Earth influences the **moon** and other less massive objects around it. When these objects are farther away from Earth or any other large body, they experience less gravity.

Objects in space experience gravity from the massive objects near them. Astronauts in the International Space Station live in a seemingly gravity-free environment. They float and are weightless. This seems to suggest that there is no gravity affecting them. However, that is not the case. They still experience a pull from gravity. Astronauts float because the station and the astronauts are in free fall toward Earth.

Newton's first law explains that an object in motion will stay in motion. All orbiting objects are in free fall—gravity is pulling them to Earth constantly. But they are also moving forward. If they move forward fast enough, they never fall to Earth, even though Earth's gravity is pulling them down. When the station was built, its speed was calibrated so that it could **orbit** Earth without falling back to it.

This same principle applies to the orbit of planets around the **sun**. The planets are moving at a particular speed, and the sun's gravitational pull is acting on the planet. As the planet moves farther from the sun, the force of gravity decreases.

As a result, generally, the paths of orbiting objects are not exact circles. Sometimes the paths are elongated, resulting in a shape called an ellipse. The moon's orbit is nearly circular.

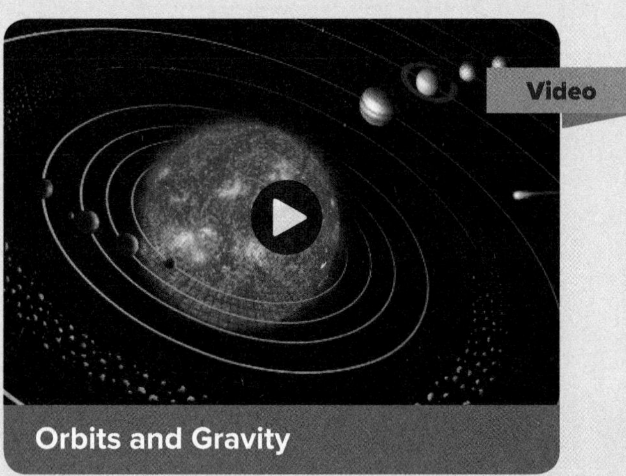

Orbits and Gravity

Now, go back through the reading on gravity. **Highlight** any parts that describe cause-and-effect relationships. Then, **use** the graphic organizer to indicate three examples of cause-and-effect relationships based on the text.

Topic: ____

Cause		**Effect**
	→	
	→	
	→	

Activity 9

Interpret Data

Quick Code
ca8303s

Planet Data

Read the text about planet data. Then, **answer** the questions that follow.

EXPLORE

Planet Data

What do you know about the planets in our solar system? They may seem small in images and models, but so does a large building when you view it from an airplane. When you are next to the building, it appears very large. Similarly, the planets in our solar system are also very large, but we have a difficult time judging their actual size because they are so far away. Exactly how large are they? Study the planetary data summarized in the table that follows to help you formulate an answer. This model of the solar system shows the planets in static orbits.

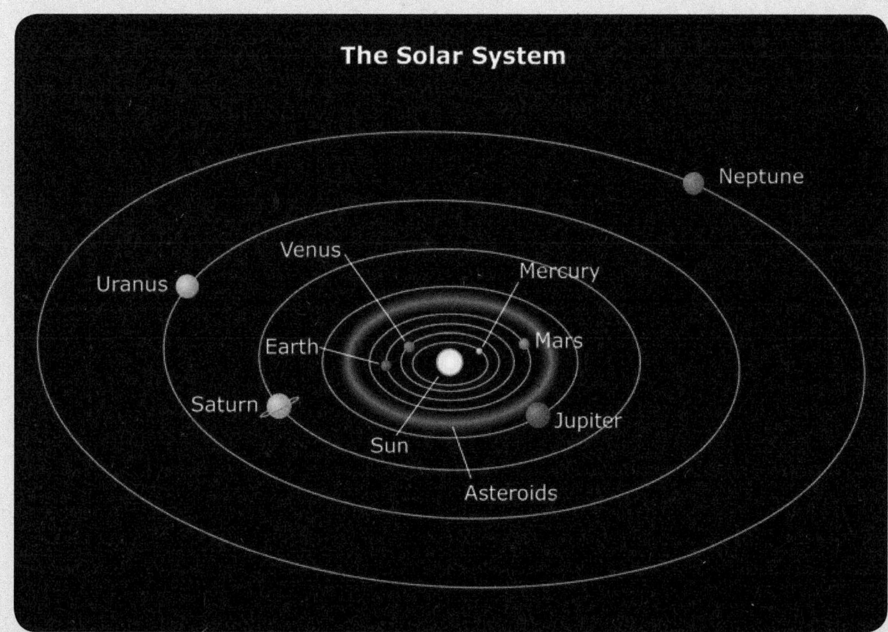

SEP Using Mathematics and Computational Thinking

Planet Data *cont'd*

If you judge size by diameter, which planet is largest and which is smallest? According to the data, Jupiter has the largest diameter and Mercury has the smallest diameter. Suppose you used mass to compare the sizes of the planets. According to the data, which planet has the greatest mass? The smallest mass? You can see that the planet with the greatest mass is Jupiter, and the planet with the smallest mass is Mercury. With respect to both diameter and mass, these two planets represent the upper and lower limits of planet size.

Use the data in the table to make some other observations about the planets. For example, is there a relationship between distance from the sun and planet size? What does that indicate about the force of gravity between the sun and each planet? Because the force of gravity between each planet and the sun depends on the masses of the two bodies as well as the distance between them, there must be a lesser force of gravity between the sun and Neptune than between the sun and Jupiter. This statement can be justified by looking at the data—Jupiter is more massive than Neptune and is much closer to the sun.

Speaking of gravity, what do you notice about the relationship between the mass of each planet and its gravity? If you compare the data in the mass column with the data in the gravity column, you should notice that gravity increases as mass increases. As the planets increase in mass, they also increase in gravity. This is not a linear relationship because a comparison of Earth and Mars shows that Earth has 10 times the mass of Mars but about twice its gravity.

The subject of gravity is not complete without bringing in a discussion of weight. How do you think the weight of an object changes as it is moved to different planets? How is the force of gravity involved? Does the force of gravity affect both weight and mass? When you remember that weight

	Mercury	Venus	Earth	Mars	Jupiter	Saturn	Uranus	Neptune
Mass (10^{24} kg)	0.330	4.87	5.97	0.642	1898	568	86.8	102
Diameter (km)	4879	12,104	12,756	6792	142,984	120,536	51,118	49,528
Density (kg/m^3)	5427	5243	5514	3933	1326	687	1271	1638
Gravity (m/s^2)	3.7	8.9	9.8	3.7	23.1	9.0	8.7	11.0
Escape Velocity (km/s)	4.3	10.4	11.2	5.0	59.5	35.5	21.3	23.5
Rotation Period (hours)	1407.6	-5832.5	23.9	24.6	9.9	10.7	-17.2	16.1
Length of Day (hours)	4222.6	2802.0	24.0	24.7	9.9	10.7	17.2	16.1
Distance from Sun (10^6 km)	57.9	108.2	149.6	227.9	778.6	1433.5	2872.5	4495.1

EXPLORE

is a force, it makes sense that the same object has a different weight on different planets. Weight is a measure of the force of gravity acting on a certain mass. Because gravity varies from planet to planet, the weight of an object will vary from planet to planet, too. However, the object's mass remains constant. Mass is a measure of the quantity of matter in an object. This quantity does not change as you move the object. Only the gravitational force acting on its mass changes.

Finally, how could you use the planetary data to calculate the distance in light-years between Earth and Neptune, the planet farthest from the sun? Recall that a light year is the distance that light can travel in one year. This distance is equivalent to 9.46×10^{12} kilometers. To make your calculation, you could start by subtracting the distance in kilometers between Earth and the sun from the distance in kilometers between Neptune and the sun. This gives the distance in kilometers between Earth and Neptune. Then, use the definition of a light year as a conversion factor to convert kilometers to light years. The answer is a very small fraction of a light year. Considering that we know that some objects are hundreds or thousands of light years away from Earth, this calculation can give you an appreciation for just how far away some things are from us!

Answer the questions.

If you were traveling on a mission to Mars, how long could you expect to be gone from Earth? **Assume** that your spacecraft travels 100 kilometers per hour.

Using the data table, **explain** the relationship between the mass of a planet and its gravitational force.

Activity 10

Evaluate

Quick Code
ca8304s

Greater Gravity

You are part of a scientific team that is studying a new solar system in another galaxy. Here are the data that your team has collected:

The center star of the solar system has a mass of 2.0×10^{30} kilograms.

Planet A, located 521×10^{6} kilometers from the star, has a mass of 3.23×10^{24} kilograms and an orbital period of 100 days.

Planet B, located 30×10^{6} kilometers from the star, has a mass of 0.0323×10^{24} kilograms and an orbital period of 23 days.

Planet C, located $4{,}325 \times 10^{6}$ kilometers from the star, has a mass of 2.03×10^{24} kilograms and an orbital period of 565 days.

Determine the strength of the gravitational force between each of the different planets and the central star. **Write** the planets in order of greatest to least gravitational force.

Force	Planet (A, B, or C)
The greatest force	
The middle force	
The least force	

EXPLORE

How Do Gravitational Forces Impact the Motion of Earth and the Moon?

Activity 11

Observe

Quick Code ca8305s

Gravity's Role in Earth and Moon Orbit

Go online to explore what causes the moon and the planets to move in a fixed orbit.

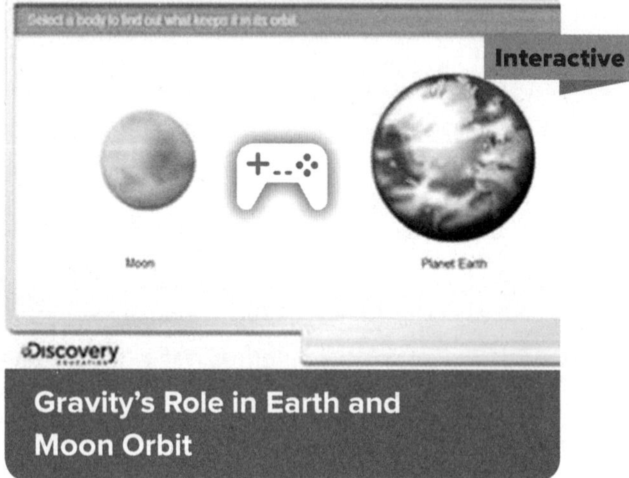

Gravity's Role in Earth and Moon Orbit

Record your data in the tables.

Record what would happen to Earth in each situation.

Sun and Earth	Gravity Only	Motion Only	Both Gravity and Motion

Record what would happen to the moon in each situation.

Earth and Moon	Gravity Only	Motion Only	Both Gravity and Motion

EXPLORE

Activity 12

Reason

Quick Code
ca8306s

Modeling the Solar System

In this activity, you will work with your class to construct a model of the solar system.

What materials do you need? (per group)

- Measuring tape
- Scrap paper
- Cardboard
- Masking tape
- Markers
- Soccer ball or basketball

Procedure

In small groups, **complete** the third column in the table. Once complete, you will **brainstorm** how to use the materials to make a scale model of the solar system.

Sample Table: Planetary Distance to the Sun

Planet	Distance from the Sun (km)	Distance from the Sun in Scale Model (1 cm: 1,000,000 km)
Mercury	57,910,000	
Venus	108,000,000	
Earth	149,600,000	
Mars	227,000,000	
Jupiter	778,330,000	
Saturn	1,429,400,000	
Uranus	2,870,970,000	
Neptune	4,504,000,000	

EXPLORE

Reflect

What was your model designed to show?

What can the model show about the solar system?

What can't the model show about the solar system?

Activity 13

Observe

Quick Code
ca8307s

Planet Nine

Watch the video, and then **answer** the question.

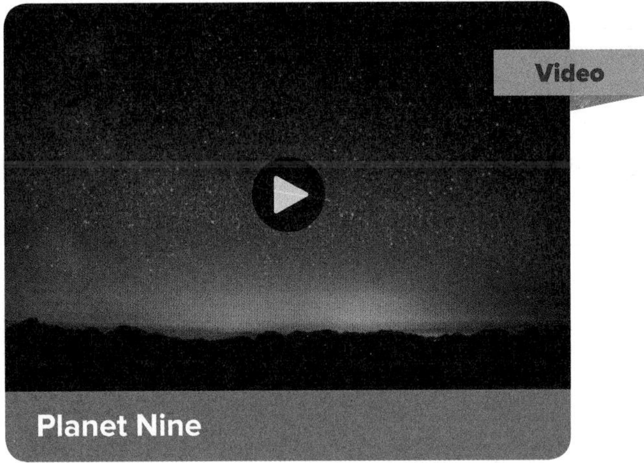

EXPLORE

Is the evidence presented in the video sufficient to justify the claim that Planet Nine exists? If not, **explain** one piece of evidence you would want in order to support the claim.

Activity 14

Evaluate

Quick Code
ca8308s

Model of Orbits

Expand on the model you created earlier by adding an unknown planet, such as a hypothetical Planet Nine. Then, **modify** your model to represent how that planet could change the pattern of other objects in the solar system over time.

SEP **Developing and Using Models**

EXPLORE

Activity 15

Record Evidence

Quick Code
ca8309s

Pluto's Moons

As you worked through this lesson, you investigated and gathered evidence about orbital forces. Now, take another look at the video Pluto's Moons, which you first saw in Engage.

How has your understanding of the video Pluto's Moons changed?

Read the Can You Explain? question from the beginning of this lesson.

Can You Explain?

How does the force of gravity move objects in the solar system?

Use your new understanding of the Pluto's Moons video to write a scientific explanation answering a question.

1. Choose a question. You may choose to answer the Can You Explain? question, or one of the questions you wrote at the start of this lesson.
2. Use the following information to help you write your explanation.

Directions: Write the Can You Explain? question in the space provided.

Use this checklist to help you plan your scientific explanation. Write your ideas in the spaces provided.

As you plan your scientific explanation, be sure to include:

- data from your investigations
- qualitative or quantitative relationships
- reliable evidence from the text
- scientific laws that apply to the real-world phenomenon
- statements indicating why the data or evidence supports your claim

Write the Question for Your Explanation

SEP **Constructing Explanations and Designing Solutions**

EXPLAIN

Create a scientific explanation for the question. This combines the claim that was made, the evidence that was collected, and a justification for why the evidence supports the claim (logical reasoning). The explanation should contain clear thoughts and accurate scientific vocabulary.

EXPLAIN

STEM in Action

Activity 16
Analyze

Quick Code
ca8310s

Careers and Gravity

Read the text about Laser Interferometer Gravitational-Wave Observatory (LIGO). **Underline** key details as you read.

Careers and Gravity

What exactly is **gravity**, and how fast does it travel? Who was right: Einstein or Newton? The video focuses on research at the Laser Interferometer Gravitational-Wave Observatory (LIGO) in Livingston, Louisiana, where scientists have constructed a sprawling facility dedicated to the detection of minute changes in space and time caused by gravitational waves.

In February 2016, LIGO scientists announced that they had made an extraordinary discovery. They actually detected gravitational waves. These are ripples in space-time that were created when two black holes merged more than a billion years ago. Based on computer models, the scientists were able to determine that one of the black holes had a mass equivalent to 29 suns, while the other's mass was equivalent to 36 suns. This collision of cosmic proportions was large enough to bend the fabric of our universe.

Even so, the distortion that LIGO detected was incredibly small. It was about one-thousandth the size of a proton, and it occurred in a matter of milliseconds. This tiny blip proves an important part of Einstein's **theory** of relativity. It also proves that scientific instruments such as LIGO are capable of measuring large events in outer space.

Can you imagine working with a team of scientists that is able to make such observations? What other events might you witness? Can you think of other careers that need to have knowledge of gravity?

Working Like a Scientist

Imagine that you are a LIGO scientist and are detecting gravitational waves created by large-scale cosmic events. These could include black holes merging, massive stars colliding, or supernovas (the explosion of a massive **star** at the end of its life). Your job is to determine the relative size of these events based on the data that have been collected from the LIGO instrument.

Cosmic Events

The data are for three cosmic events. They show the amount of time it takes the laser to travel to each of the two wings of the LIGO instrument.

Event	Time to Wing #1 (milliseconds)	Time to Wing #2 (milliseconds)
A	3.0	3.5
B	3.2	4.3
C	4.1	4.8

Based on the data in the table, **write** the events in order from smallest (left) to largest (right) .

Explain

Explain your reasoning.

ELABORATE

Activity 17

Concept Review

Review: Orbital Forces

Quick Code
ca8311s

Now that you have completed the objectives for this concept, review the core ideas you have learned. Record some of the core ideas in the space provided.

Core Ideas

Talk with a Group

Now, think about the Diamond Planet video you saw in Get Started. Discuss how what you've learned about orbital forces can help you understand the diamond planet.

EVALUATE

CONCEPT

2.4

Energy in the Universe

Student Objectives

By the end of this lesson:

- [ ] I can construct explanations of how noncontact forces affect small and large objects in our solar system.
- [ ] I can develop and refine a model that describes energy conversions among objects in the solar system on both the macro scale and the micro scale.
- [ ] I can use mathematics and computational thinking to calculate changes in kinetic energy for objects in the solar system.

Key Vocabulary

elliptical, force, fusion, kinetic energy

Quick Code
ca8328s

Activity 1

Can You Explain?

How does energy from the sun reach the surface of Earth?

Quick Code
ca8312s

Activity 2

Ask Questions

Quick Code
ca8313s

Gravity and Orbits

In this solar system, planets are kept in their orbits based on the gravitational pull of the sun. The spin of the planets is maintained in a certain orbit based on the forces around it. **Think** about the force of a spinning object.

Examine the image of spinning fire. If the lines in the spinning art image represent objects that are ejected into other parts of the solar system, what happens to those objects? Do they break apart due to gravitational forces? Do they transfer their kinetic energy to another form of energy? Do they collide with other objects? In this image, you can observe the particles being pulled to Earth by gravity and the mechanical force applied by the person to put the fire in motion.

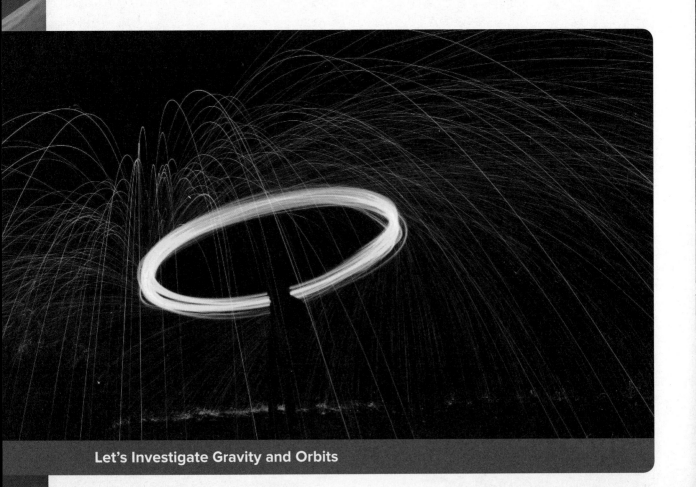

Let's Investigate Gravity and Orbits

ENGAGE

How could the force of magnetism be used to change the output of the spin art if you used metallic paint instead of fire?

How do you think the picture would change if the speed of the spin slowed?

If the lines in the spinning art image represent objects that are ejected into other parts of the solar system, what happens to those objects?

What questions do you have about gravity and orbits?

Activity 3
Analyze

Quick Code
ca8314s

Colliding Galaxies

Read the following text.

Colliding Galaxies

Have you ever tried to swing a ball on a string around your head? Did the ball travel in a circle or an **elliptical** shape? What did you have to do to prevent the ball from falling to the ground? Without sufficient speed, the **force** of Earth's gravity will pull the ball to the ground. Are you providing energy to the system? The sun's gravitational pull stabilizes the elliptical orbits of the planets in our solar system. What energy is added to the system to keep the planets in orbit?

If the lines in the spinning art image represent objects that are ejected into other parts of the solar system, what happens to those objects? Do they break apart due to gravitational forces? Do they transfer their **kinetic energy** to another form of energy? Do they collide with other objects?

Did you know that galaxies can collide? Can you imagine what that would look like? It would mean billions of stars smashing into billions of stars. What would happen? Would a new galaxy be formed, or would the stars be destroyed in the process? Would this explosion ripple through space and affect other galaxies?

It is an extraordinary event to try to picture. Yet, scientists are certain that such collisions take place. The merger of two galaxies can take hundreds of millions of years. In these cases, it is infrequent for stars to actually collide because of the large distances between the stars in both galaxies.

ENGAGE

Choose one of the following questions from the text to make predictions:

- What would happen if galaxies collided?
- If galaxies collided, would a new galaxy be formed?
- If galaxies collided, would the stars be destroyed?
- If galaxies collided, would the explosion ripple through space and affect other galaxies?

Write down what you already know about the answer to the question you chose.

SEP **Asking Questions and Defining Problems**

Create your own questions about what happens when galaxies in space collide. **Write** your response.

You can look for answers to your questions throughout the remainder of the concept. If your questions are not answered within the concept, use reliable research sources to discover answers to your questions.

Activity 4

Evaluate

Quick Code
ca8315s

ENGAGE

What Do You Already Know About Energy in the Universe?

How Energy Transforms

For each scenario described, **identify** the energy transformation that occurs. **Write** the correct energy transformation into each space provided to complete the sentence.

kinetic energy	light energy	sound energy
electrical energy	chemical energy	heat energy

A person rubs their hands together and the hands heat up.

________________ to ________________

A hammer strikes a piano string and a note sounds out.

________________ to ________________

A battery causes electricity to flow through a circuit.

________________ to ________________

A dark shirt sits out in the sun and becomes hot.

________________ to ________________

Using what you've learned, **brainstorm** some examples of energy transformations.

Transfer of Energy

Match each scenario to the energy transformation that it best represents. **Draw** a line between each scenario and its matching energy transformation.

Scenario	Energy Transformation
Symphony playing in a concert hall	Gravitational to Electrical
Plankton whose body can produce light	Chemical to Kinetic
Waterfall powering a factory	Chemical to Light
Pumping gas in a car before a trip	Kinetic to Sound

ENGAGE

Terms of the Universe

Use the following terms to write a statement: *universe*, *galaxy*, *stars*, *planets*. Your statement should describe how the terms relate to one another in some way.

Sketch a drawing that illustrates your statement in the space provided.

What Is the Kinetic Energy of Objects in the Solar System?

Activity 5
Analyze

Quick Code
ca8316s

Noncontact Forces

Read the following text.

Noncontact Forces

Can you identify which noncontact **force** is included in each image? What do gravitational, electrical forces, and magnetic forces have in common?

Magnetic forces can attract particles, electrical forces can move particles toward one another, and gravity pulls objects to the center of mass of another object. So, why doesn't Earth collide with other objects? Why don't we feel the impact of these forces acting in the solar system? How do these forces balance each other in the solar system? Our solar system is unique in the near circular orbit shapes of its main planets.

The force of gravity, electrical charges, and magnetism can all be applied to place objects in motion. Each of these noncontact forces affects both small and large objects on Earth and in the solar system. Objects in motion stay in motion unless acted upon by a force. Newton's laws also tell us that an object at rest will stay at rest until acted upon by a force. In the solar system, objects are in constant motion. Particles and larger objects collide with one another, and we can observe those collisions in different ways.

Noncontact Force #1

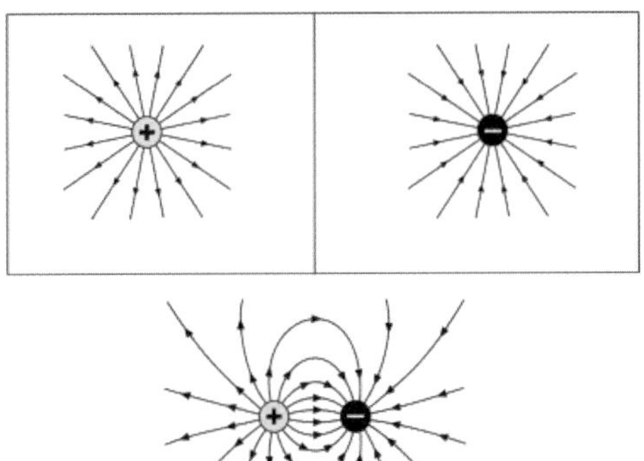

Noncontact Force #2

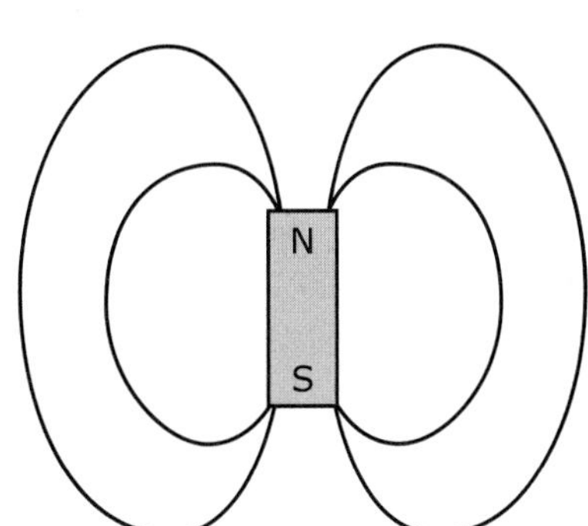

Noncontact Force #3

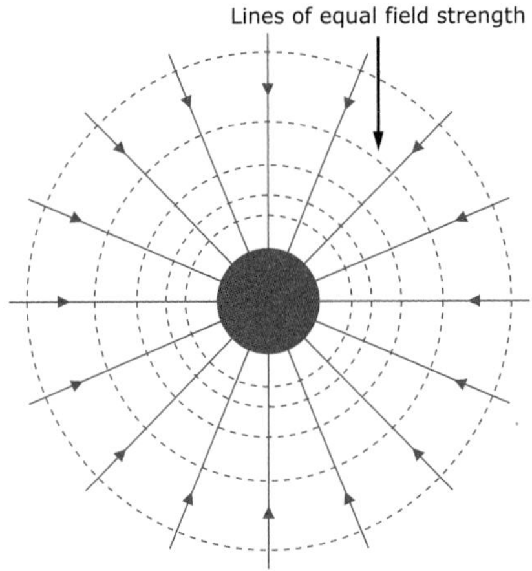

Look at each of the images. Can you identify which noncontact force is included in each image? What do gravitational, electrical forces, and magnetic forces have in common?

Be prepared to later explain your reasoning to a partner and then think of a question to constructively critique your partner's reasoning.

What do gravitational, electrical, and magnetic forces have in common?

EXPLORE

Activity 6
Analyze

Quick Code
ca8317s

Kinetic Energy

Read the following text.

Kinetic Energy

Think of the solar system as a complex system of many objects in motion. When analyzing forces and energy in systems, you will find it helpful to define boundaries of the system. For example, when considering how the forces of gravity, electrical force, and magnetic forces interact in the solar system, consider the sun to be the center of the system and the only other objects in the system to be planets orbiting the sun.

We know that within this system, due to its mass, the sun exerts a strong gravitational force attracting each planet to its center of mass. Each of the planets is also in motion, which means that each possesses **kinetic energy**. Remember that the kinetic energy of an object is dependent on the mass of the object and its velocity.

$$KE = \frac{mv^2}{2}$$

The velocity of a planet in orbit is generally faster as it moves closer to the sun, due to its orbit being **elliptical**. If the mass of the planet stays the same, and the velocity increases, what happens to the kinetic energy of the planet? For example, we know that the mass of Earth is 5.972×10^{24} kilograms and the velocity of Earth when it is closest to the sun is 30.29 kilometers per second. What is the kinetic energy of Earth at that point in its orbit?

SEP **Using Mathematics and Computational Thinking**

We know that Earth orbits the sun due to the gravitational force of the sun. Technically, planets and stars orbit around their common center of mass. Center of mass is the exact center of all the matter in which an object is made of. For spherical objects, such as planets, the center of mass is in the center of the object. In space, two or more objects, such as Earth and the moon, can be considered a system. In this system, due to the differences in the mass of Earth compared with the moon, the center of mass for the system will be closest to Earth (the larger mass). If we think of the moon and Earth as a system, how does the kinetic energy of this system compare with the kinetic energy of Earth on its own?

EXPLORE

Using the formula for kinetic energy, **calculate** the kinetic energy of Earth based on the data provided in the text. **Write** your answer.

Activity 7

Interpret Data

Kinetic Energy of Orbits

Quick Code
ca8318s

In this investigation, you will investigate the relationship between a planet's distance from the sun and the speed at which it travels in its orbit.

Predict

What do you predict you will find out about the relationship between a planet's speed and its distance from the sun? **Write** your prediction.

What materials do you need? (per group)

- Graph paper

Procedure

1. On graphing paper, set up a line graph.
2. Label the horizontal axis "Average Distance from the Sun (AU)" and the vertical axis "Average Speed (km/s)."
3. Use the data in the following table to plot a point for each planet.

Planet	Average Distance from the Sun (AU)	Average Speed (km/s)
Mercury	0.4	48.1
Venus	0.7	34.9
Earth	1.0	29.8
Mars	1.5	24.1
Jupiter	5.2	13.0
Saturn	9.5	9.7
Uranus	19.2	6.8
Neptune	30.1	5.4

Reflect

What general rule relates the distance of a planet from the sun to that planet's speed in its orbit?

The dwarf planet Ceres orbits the sun at an average distance of 2.8 AU. Plot the point that would represent Ceres on the graph. What is the average speed of Ceres?

The dwarf planet Pluto orbits at an average distance from the sun of 39.5 AU. Extrapolating from your graph, what is Pluto's average orbital speed?

Suppose an amateur astronomer discovers an asteroid that is moving at a speed of about 8 kilometers per second. She estimates that it must be about 13.5 AU from the sun. Based on your graph, does the pattern of planetary speeds and distance support or fail to support her estimated distance?

Why do you think that the planets that are closer to the sun have to travel at higher speeds than the more distant planets?

Earth is closest to the sun in January and farthest from the sun in July. During which month is Earth moving fastest in its orbit? When is it moving slowest? Explain your answer.

EXPLORE

Comets have long, elliptical orbits that bring them close to the sun and carry them out to great distances. How does the speed of a comet change as it orbits the sun?

Consider the graphs that you have drawn. What can you tell about the kinetic energy of each planet as it moves through its orbit?

Activity 8

Evaluate

Quick Code
ca8319s

Kinetic Energy in Orbits

The following data table provides the masses, maximum velocities, and orbital periods for the four inner planets. Using this data, **determine** if a linear or nonlinear pattern exists between the orbital period and the kinetic energy of the planet at its maximum velocity. Then, **calculate** the kinetic energy of each planet at its maximum velocity. **Write** your response in the space provided.

Planet	Mass (10^{24} kg)	Maximum velocity (km/s)	Orbital period (days)
Mercury	0.330	48.1	88.0
Venus	4.87	34.9	224.7
Earth	5.97	29.8	365.2
Mars	0.642	24.1	687.0

EXPLORE

How Is Energy Transferred in the Solar System?

Activity 9

Analyze

Quick Code
ca8320s

Sun's Release of Energy

Read the following text and **view** the images and videos. Then, **complete** the activity that follows.

Sun's Release of Energy

The sun's energy comes from its core. Hydrogen is found within the sun's core. There, it is converted into helium. This process is called nuclear **fusion**. Nuclear energy is a type of potential energy. Due to the massive gravitational pull of the sun, energy from its core takes thousands of years to get to its surface.

However, some of the energy moves to the sun's surface. This is where it is released into space. The sun releases energy as electromagnetic radiation.

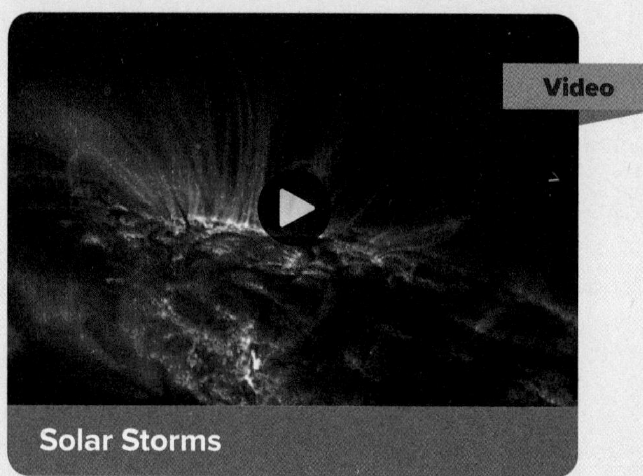

Video

Solar Storms

SEP Developing and Using Models

CCC Energy and Matter

These charged particles of energy take two forms that we notice—heat and light.

The sun has magnetic fields that extend from two poles, but it also has magnetic fields that arc back onto the surface of the sun. Most of these smaller magnetic fields interact with each other. When this occurs, solar flares radiate charged electric particles into the solar system. These particles travel at high speeds and collide with other forces and objects their path.

For those planets that possess magnetic fields, the sun's electric particles travel along the magnetic fields emitted from planetary objects. For those planets without magnetic fields, such as Mars, the electric particles can more easily enter their atmosphere, causing extreme temperatures on the surface of the planet.

EXPLORE

Sun and Earth Subsystem

To analyze the interaction of magnetic and electric forces between the sun and Earth, we need to set the boundaries of our system of Earth, the sun, and the moon. When the charged electric particles from the sun move in the direction of Earth, Earth's magnetosphere buffers Earth and the electric particles travel along Earth's magnetic fields.

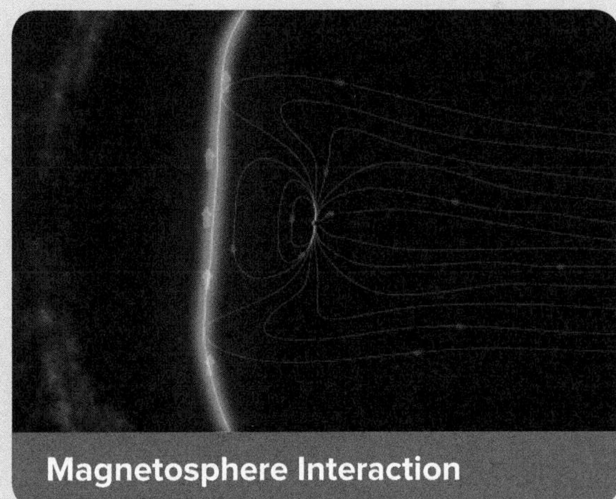

Magnetosphere Interaction

Energy in the system is converted from the potential nuclear energy that produced the magnetic energy that caused the solar flares on the sun, to the **kinetic energy** of the charged particles, to the thermal energy as some particles enter the atmosphere and heat Earth. Energy in the total system is conserved because some of the energy that does not reach Earth's surface is converted to light, kinetic energy, and heat energy outside of the magnetosphere.

We can observe the interaction between the electric and magnetic forces in what we call an aurora. In Earth's Northern Hemisphere, this aurora is called the Northern Lights. These strong periods of electric energy interactions with the magnetosphere can disable some communication technology devices for brief periods of time. Some particles travel at the appropriate wavelength to enter Earth's atmosphere. These charged particles are thermal energy from the sun.

Cause of Northern Lights

Using what you have learned, **develop** an energy flow model that shows the energy flow between the sun, Earth, and the moon. **Include** both the macroscale (changes in kinetic energy of Earth within its orbit) and the microscale (electric particles moving along magnetic field lines and their conversion to thermal energy). You can either **sketch** your model on paper or **make** a physical model. **Use** the following diagram to help you get started.

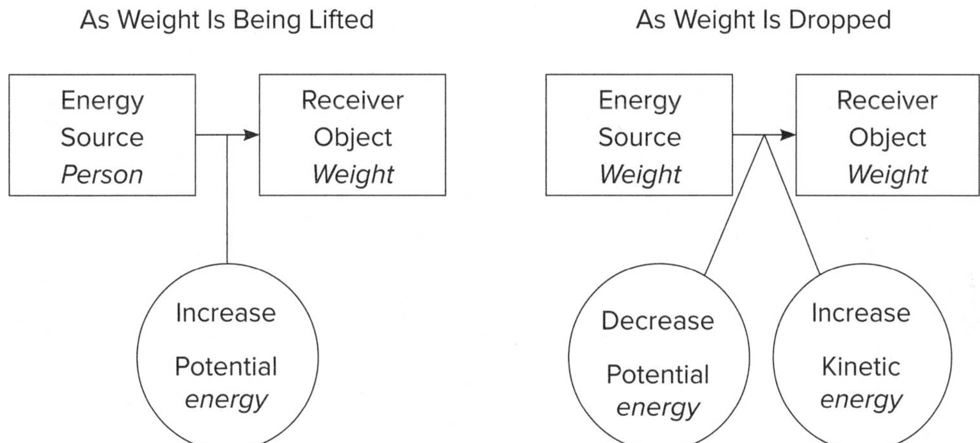

EXPLORE

Activity 10

Evaluate

Compass as a Model

Quick Code
ca8321s

Consider the following model of a compass interacting with a magnet. How does this model compare with the interaction of noncontact forces in the sun-Earth-moon systems? **Write** your response in the space provided.

System

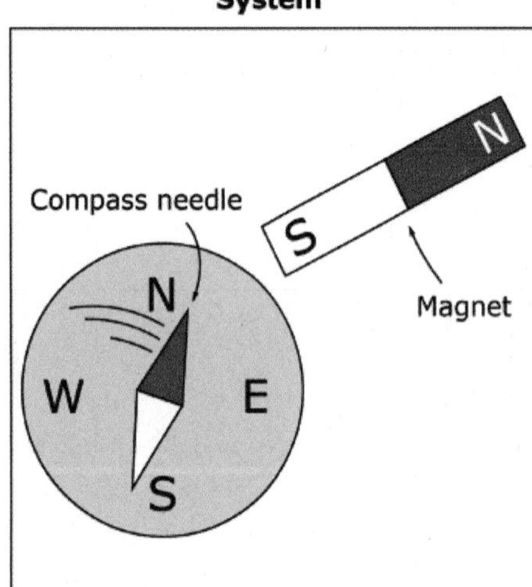

Model of energy flow within the system

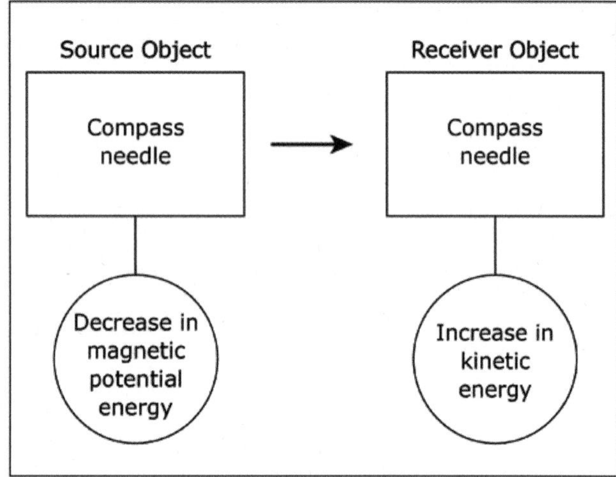

Evaluate and **propose** revisions to the model to indicate the conversion of energy within the solar system. **Write** your response.

EXPLORE

Activity 11

Record Evidence

Quick Code
ca8322s

Gravity and Orbits

As you worked through this lesson, you investigated and gathered evidence about energy in the universe. Now, take another look at the image Gravity and Orbits, which you first saw in Engage.

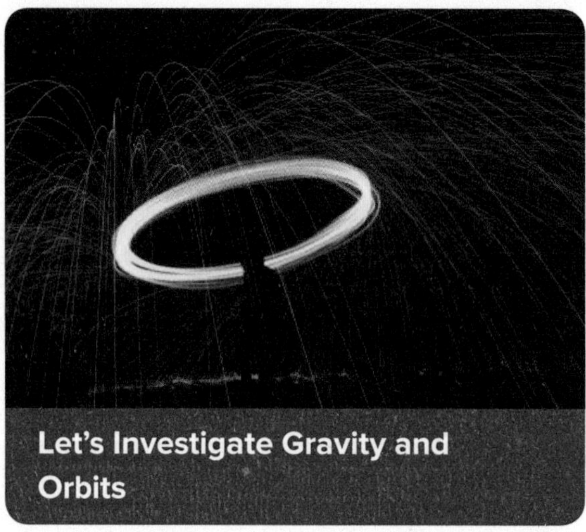

Let's Investigate Gravity and Orbits

How has your understanding of the Gravity and Orbits image changed?

Read the Can You Explain? question from the beginning of this lesson.

Can You Explain?

How does energy from the sun reach the surface of Earth?

Use your new understanding of Gravity and Orbits to write a scientific explanation answering a question.

1. Choose a question. You may choose to answer the Can You Explain? question, or one of the questions you wrote at the start of this lesson.
2. Use the following information to help you write your explanation.

Use this checklist to help you plan your scientific explanation. Write your ideas in the spaces provided.

As you plan your scientific explanation, be sure to include:

- data from your investigations
- qualitative or quantitative relationships
- reliable evidence from the text
- scientific laws that apply to the real-world phenomenon
- statements indicating why the data or evidence supports your claim

Using your notes, write your scientific explanation for your question in the space provided here.

EXPLAIN

SEP **Constructing Explanations and Designing Solutions**

STEM in Action

Activity 12
Analyze

Quick Code
ca8323s

Reading the Stars

Read the following text and **view** the images and videos. Then, **fill in** the table that follows.

Reading the Stars

Astronomers observe the sky with sophisticated telescopes that are based on Earth and also launched in space. Astrophysicists gather and evaluate the data from many different sources. Their goal is to build a coherent picture of the universe by integrating the scientific evidence with the laws of physics. The knowledge of distant galaxies, supernovae, and solar systems similar to our own is derived from observation and interpretation of data transmitted back from the detectors carried by spacecraft.

Introduction to Space Science

Probes carry instrumentation that beams information back to Earth. Some probes have flown past other planets and have exited the solar system. They will not come back to Earth.

SEP Obtaining, Evaluating, and Communicating Information

The Cassini probe is still orbiting Saturn and transmitting data. You may have heard of the Curiosity mission to Mars. The term *satellites* usually refers to probes that orbit our planet. Space engineers design spacecraft that can withstand the rigors of launching and traveling in space. Materials scientists develop alloys and other composite materials that can survive radiation and the intense cold of space.

How does a star release energy? How fast and in what direction is it moving? What is the chemical composition of a planet? These are questions that astrophysicists ask. Many answers come from the information instruments carried by spacecraft gather and relay to Earth. Much information comes from the emission spectra of celestial bodies. In astronomy, the term *emission spectrum* describes a graph that shows how much electromagnetic radiation is released over a range of wavelengths, from radio waves to X-rays to gamma rays.

For example, the Galileo space probe, which flew by Jupiter and its moons, carried several spectrometers that recorded emissions in the near infrared, visible, and ultraviolet regions of the spectrum. On Earth, spectroscopists studied and interpreted the spectra that were recorded and transmitted back to Earth by the instruments on the probe.

Galileo Explores Io, Ganymede, Callisto, and Europa

ELABORATE

Using what you've learned, **choose** a probe and **research** its speed and composition. **Explain** how advances in technology influence the progress of science. **Fill in** the chart.

Speed of the Probe	Composition of the Probe	Advances in Technology Influence the Progress of Science

Probing a Probe

Use this information to further research one of the probes you've just learned about. **Write** about your probe, providing the following information:

- When the probe was launched
- The mission or goals of the probe
- The date its mission was completed
- At least two problems or technology-related issues that were encountered during the mission
- How scientists and/or engineers resolved—or attempted to resolve—each problem or issue
- Whether the probe achieved its goals, and why or why not

ELABORATE

Activity 13

Concept Review

Review: Energy in the Universe

Quick Code
ca8324s

Now that you have completed the objectives for this concept, review the core ideas you have learned. Record some of the core ideas in the space provided.

Core Ideas

Talk with a Group

Now, think about the Diamond Planet video you saw in Get Started. Discuss how what you've learned about energy in the universe can help you understand the diamond planet.

EVALUATE

Solve Problems

Quick Code
ca8326s

Unit Project: Exoplanet Follow-Up

How can we confirm the existence of an exoplanet and further explore it?

In this project, you will design a technological tool that could be used to verify the existence of this exoplanet. You will also investigate other questions, such as whether the planet has liquid water on its surface.

Planet GJ 436b

SEP Constructing Explanations and Designing Solutions

SEP Obtaining, Evaluating, and Communicating Information

CCC Cause and Effect

The nearest exoplanet that has been discovered is Proxima B. It was discovered in 2016. It appears to be a rocky planet within the habitable zone of Proxima Centauri. Proxima Centauri is the closest star to our solar system. The planet has a mass that is at least 1.3 times the mass of Earth. It orbits around its host star roughly every 11.2 Earth days. Unfortunately, Proxima Centauri is a red dwarf star. As a result, scientists doubt that Proxima B would be habitable. Specifically, the variation in light and the type of light from Proxima Centauri could make it difficult for life to thrive there.

Scientists, engineers, and entrepreneurs are pushing ahead to observe the potential planets in the Alpha Centauri system. Proxima Centauri is one of three stars in this system. These missions have included Breakthrough Starshot and Mission Centaur. Breakthrough Starshot involves sending tiny probes to the star system. Mission Centaur involves launching a lightweight telescope to directly image a planet in the Alpha Centauri system.

Use the Student Engineering Design sheet to help you plan your design.

Student Engineering Design Sheet

Define the Problem

- What is the problem you are trying to solve?
- What are some initial ideas on how to solve the problem?
- Which of the proposed solutions deserve further investigation?

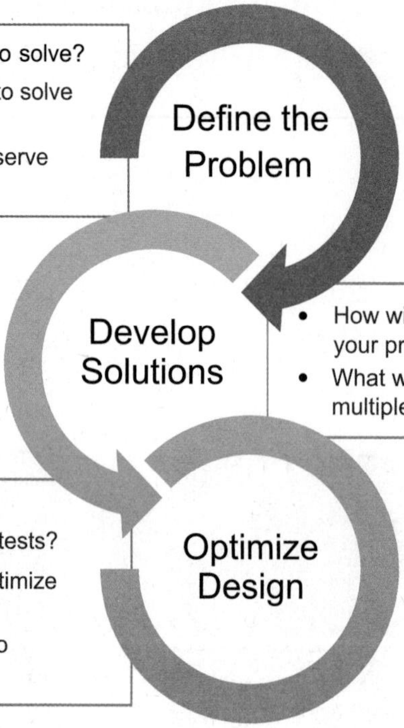

Develop Solutions

- How will you construct and test your proposed solution?
- What were the results of your multiple tests?

Optimize Design

- What changes will you make to your proposed solution, as a result of your tests?
- What new tests will you conduct to optimize your proposed solution?
- What is your final proposed solution to the problem?

Data from Proxima B

Propose a technological tool that could be used to further investigate/confirm the existence of the exoplanet Proxima B. You can be creative and do not need to consider constraints such as money and size. **Describe** how your apparatus would be able to collect further data about Proxima B.

ide 8 Glossary

English — **A** — Español

acceleration
a change in the velocity (speed, direction, or both) of a body (related word: accelerate)

aceleración
cambio en la velocidad (rapidez, dirección o ambas) de un cuerpo
(palabra relacionada: acelerar)

---

air
the part of the atmosphere closest to Earth; the part of the atmosphere that organisms on Earth use for respiration

aire
parte de la atmósfera más cercana a la Tierra; la parte de la atmósfera que los organismos que habitan la Tierra utilizan para respirar

---

allele
one member of a pair or series of genes on specific chromosomes in specific positions

alelo
uno de los miembros de un par o serie de genes en cromosomas específicos en posiciones específicas

---

amber
a fossil resin from tree sap, usually a translucent, yellow-brown color, which may contain insects or other organisms

ámbar
resina fósil de un árbol, por lo general es translúcido, de color marrón amarillento; puede contener insectos u otros organismos.

---

amino acid
one of the 20 types of molecules that combine to form proteins

aminoácido
uno de los 20 tipos de moléculas que se combinan para formar proteínas

---

amplitude
height or “strength” of a wave

amplitud
altura o “fuerza” de una onda

---

antibiotic
a chemical that kills or inhibits growth of bacteria

antibiótico
un químico que mata o inhibe el crecimiento de bacterias

---

aquatic
relating to water

acuático
relativo al agua

Grade 8 **Glossary**

asteroid
a small object made of rock or metal that orbits the sun

asteroide
pequeño objeto de roca o metal que orbita alrededor del sol

---

atmosphere
the layers of gases that surround a planet

atmósfera
capas de gases que rodean un planeta

---

attract (magnetism)
the action between two opposing magnetic poles

atraer (magnetismo)
la acción entre dos polos magnéticos opuestos

---

axis
an imaginary line that an object spins or revolves around

eje
línea imaginaria sobre la cual gira o da vueltas un objeto

B

backbone
the column of bones that runs along the backs of all vertebrate animals and protects the spinal cord

espina dorsal
columna de huesos que se extiende a lo largo de la espalda de todos los animales vertebrados y protege la médula espinal

---

bacteria
single-celled organisms without an organized nucleus
(related terms: bacterium, prokaryote)

bacterias
organismos unicelulares sin un núcleo organizado (términos relacionados: bacteria, procariota)

---

biodiversity
the many different types of life that exist in an environment

biodiversidad
muchos y diferentes tipos de vida que existen en un medioambiente

---

biosphere
that part of Earth in which life can exist

biosfera
parte de la Tierra donde puede existir la vida

C

carbon
an element that is found in almost all compounds that make up living things

carbono
elemento que se encuentra en casi todos los compuestos que forman seres vivos

---

carbon dioxide
a waste product made by cells of the body; a gas in the air made of carbon and oxygen atoms: Humans rid themselves of carbon dioxide waste by exhaling, or breathing out.

dióxido de carbono
desecho formado por células del cuerpo; gas del aire formado por átomos de carbono y oxígeno: los humanos desechamos dióxido de carbono al exhalar o expulsar aire

---

cast
a type of fossil formed when sediment fills a mold of an organic object such as a fossil shell, creating a replica of that object made of sediment

calco
tipo de fósil formado cuando el sedimento llena un molde de un objeto orgánico, como una concha fósil y crea una réplica del objeto hecha de sedimento

---

Celsius
the metric temperature scale: Water boils at 100 degrees Celsius, and it freezes at 0 degrees Celsius

Celsius
escala de la temperatura métrica: el agua hierve a los 100 grados centígrados y se congela a los 0 grados centígrados

---

characteristic
a feature of an organism; something you can observe about an organism

característica
rasgo de un organismo; algo que se puede observar sobre un organismo

---

chlorophyll
a green pigment found in photosynthetic organisms

clorofila
pigmento verde que atrapa la energía del sol

---

climate
the average weather conditions in an area (related word: climatic)

clima
condiciones promedio del tiempo atmosférico en un área (palabra relacionada: climático)

comet
a body of ice and dust that travels in a long narrow orbit around the sun

cometa
cuerpo de hielo y polvo que viaja en una órbita larga y estrecha alrededor del sol

---

conservation of energy
Energy cannot be created out of nothing, nor can it be completely destroyed. Energy can only change its form.

conservación de energía
La energía no se puede crear de la nada, y tampoco se la puede destruir por completo. La energía solo puede cambiar de forma.

---

contact
the act of touching. Two things are in contact when they are touching one another.

contacto
acto de tocar. Dos cosas están en contacto cuando se tocan entre sí.

---

core
the innermost layer of Earth, comprised of the liquid outer core and solid inner core; consists mainly of iron and nickel

núcleo
capa más interna de la Tierra, consta del núcleo externo líquido y el núcleo interno sólido; constituido principalmente por hierro y níquel

---

crater
a large, circular pit in the surface of a planet or other body in space usually formed when two bodies in space collide

cráter
hoyo grande y circular en la superficie de un planeta u otro cuerpo en el espacio, generalmente formado cuando chocan dos cuerpos en el espacio

D

decay
to break down or wear away

pudrirse
descomponerse o desgastarse

---

deciduous forest
a forest containing trees that lose their leaves each year

bosque caduco
bosque que contiene árboles que pierden las hojas cada año

---

deforestation
the clearing, by burning or logging, of trees in a forested area

deforestación
desmonte, por quema o tala, de árboles en un área forestal

density
an object's mass divided by its volume; a measure of how many particles are packed together into a certain amount of space
(related word: dense)

densidad
masa de un objeto dividida por su volumen; medida que indica en qué forma se comprimen las partículas en cierta cantidad de espacio
(palabra relacionada: denso)

---

diameter
the length of a straight line that runs from one side of a circle (or sphere), through the middle of the circle (or sphere), to the other side; the width of a circle or sphere through its middle

diámetro
longitud de una línea recta que corre desde un lado de un círculo (o esfera), a través del medio del círculo (o esfera), hasta el otro lado; el ancho de un círculo o esfera a través de su medio

---

diffraction
the bending of light or sound waves around obstacles in its path

difracción
la desviación de ondas de luz o sonido alrededor de los obstáculos en su camino

---

disease
a condition that disrupts processes in the body

enfermedad
afección que perturba los procesos del cuerpo

DNA
found in the nucleus of a cell, a long nucleic acid molecule containing the genetic instructions for the development and functioning of all living organisms; abbreviation for deoxyribonucleic acid

ADN
molécula larga de ácido nucleico que se encuentra en el núcleo de una célula y que contiene las instrucciones genéticas para el desarrollo y funcionamiento de todos los organismos vivos; es la abreviatura de ácido desoxirribonucleico

---

drought
a prolonged shortage of rainfall

sequía
falta prolongada de lluvia

---

dwarf planet
a body in space that orbits the sun; similar to a small planet but without the proper mass

planeta enano
un cuerpo en el espacio que orbita alrededor del sol; similar a un planeta pequeño pero sin la masa adecuada

E

Earth the third planet from the sun; the planet on which we live (related words: earthly; earth - meaning soil or dirt)	**Tierra** tercer planeta desde el sol; planeta en el cual vivimos (palabras relacionadas: terrenal; tierra en el sentido de suelo o suciedad)
echo a sound wave that bounces off of a surface and reflects back to the source	**eco** onda sonora que rebota en una superficie y se refleja de regreso a la fuente
ecosystem all the living and nonliving things in an area that interact with each other	**ecosistema** todos los seres vivos y los elementos no vivos en un área que interaccionan entre sí
electric having to do with electricity; a form of energy commonly used for lights, electric motors, and heating	**eléctrico** que tiene relación con la electricidad; forma de energía comúnmente usada para luces, motores eléctricos y calor
electromagnet a metal object that acts as a magnet when an electric current moves through it	**electroimán** objeto de metal que actúa como un imán cuando una corriente eléctrica se mueve a través de él
electromagnetic spectrum the full range of frequencies of electromagnetic waves	**espectro electromagnético** rango completo de frecuencias de las ondas electromagnéticas
elliptical shaped like an oval	**elíptico** con forma ovalada

embryo
an early stage in the growth of an organism in which the organism is made up of a small number of cells and contained within a protective structure such as a seed or uterus

embrión
primera etapa en el desarrollo de un organismo en la cual el organismo está formado por un pequeño número de células y se encuentra en el interior de una estructura protectora, como una semilla o un útero

---

endangered species
a species that is in danger of extinction due to its low number of remaining individuals

especie en peligro de extinción
una especie que se encuentra en peligro de extinción debido a su bajo número de individuos restantes

---

energy
the ability to do work or cause change; the ability to move an object some distance

energía
habilidad para hacer un trabajo o producir un cambio; habilidad para mover un objeto a cierta distancia

---

environment
all the living and nonliving things that surround an organism

medio ambiente
todos los seres vivos y objetos sin vida que rodean a un organismo

---

equator
an imaginary line that divides Earth into Northern and Southern Hemispheres; located halfway between the North and South Poles
(related word: equatorial)

ecuador
línea imaginaria que divide la Tierra en Hemisferio Norte y Hemisferio Sur; ubicada a mitad de camino entre el Polo Norte y el Polo Sur
(palabra relacionada: ecuatorial)

---

evidence
data or information that either supports a statement or shows that it is not true

prueba
datos o información que respaldan un argumento o que demuestran que no es verdadero

---

evolution
A theory that the various types of animals and plants have their origin in other preexisting types and that the distinguishable differences are due to modifications in successive generations

evolución
teoría según la cual los diferentes tipos de animales y plantas provienen de otros tipos preexistentes; según esta teoría las diferencias distinguibles entre ellos se deben a los cambios que ocurren a través de generaciones sucesivas

extinct
describes a species of animals that once lived on Earth but which no longer exists (related word: extinction)

extinto
palabra que hace referencia a una especie de animales que una vez habitó la Tierra, pero que ya no existe
(palabra relacionada: extinción)

F

food chain
a model that shows one set of feeding relationships among living things

cadena alimentaria
modelo que muestra un conjunto de relaciones alimentarias entre seres vivos

---

food web
a model that shows many different feeding relationships among living things

red alimentaria
modelo que muestra muchas y diferentes relaciones de alimentación entre los seres vivos

---

force
a pull or push that is applied to an object

fuerza
acción de atraer o empujar que se aplica a un objeto

---

fossil
evidence that an organism once existed in an area; can be a part of the organism's body or a trace fossil which is a mark or print left by the organism (related word: fossilize)

fósil
muestra de que un organismo existió una vez en un área; puede ser una parte del cuerpo del organismo o un rastro fósil, que es una marca o impresión dejada por el organismo (palabra relacionada: fosilizar)

---

fossil fuels
various types of nonrenewable fuels naturally formed from the remains of plants and animals that died thousands or millions of years ago

combustibles fósiles
varios tipos de combustibles formados de manera natural a partir de los restos de plantas y animales que murieron hace miles o millones de años

---

fossil record
the information about Earth's history that can be gathered from fossils

registro fósil
información sobre la historia de la Tierra que puede reunirse a partir de los fósiles

frame of reference
an item against which the motion of an object can be measured

sistema de referencia
elemento o elementos respecto a los cuales puede medirse el movimiento de un objeto

---

frequency
the number of cycles a wave completes in a period of time; the number of times something happens in a period of time

frecuencia
cantidad de ciclos que completa una onda en un período; cantidad de veces que sucede algo en un período

---

friction
a force that opposes the motion of a body across a surface or through a gas or liquid

fricción
fuerza que se opone al movimiento de un cuerpo sobre una superficie o a través de un gas o un líquido

---

fusion
a nuclear reaction in which nuclei combine to produce more massive nuclei resulting in the release of large amounts of energy

fusión
reacción nuclear donde los núcleos se combinan para producir más núcleos masivos, que resultan en la liberación de grandes cantidades de energía

G

galaxy
a group of solar systems, dust, and gas held together by gravity; our solar system is part of the Milky Way galaxy

galaxia
grupo de sistemas solares, polvo y gas unidos por la gravedad; nuestro sistema solar es parte de la galaxia llamada Vía Láctea

---

gas
a state of matter without any defined volume or shape in which atoms or molecules move about freely

gas
estado de la materia sin volumen ni forma definidos en el cual los átomos o moléculas se mueven libremente

---

gene
the basic unit of heredity in a living organism; a segment of DNA or RNA

gen
unidad básica de la herencia en un organismo vivo; segmento de ADN o ARN

---

genetic variation
range of differences in DNA among organisms

variación genética
rango de diferencias en el ADN entre organismos

germs
disease-causing microorganisms

gérmenes
microorganismos que causan enfermedad

glacier
a large mass of ice resting on, or overlapping, a land surface

glaciar
una gran masa de hielo que descansa sobre o se superpone con una superficie terrestre

gravity
a force that exists between any two objects that have mass (related word: gravitational)

gravedad
fuerza que existe entre dos objetos cualquiera que tienen masa
(palabra relacionada: gravitacional)

greenhouse gas
a gas, usually carbon-based, that contributes to global warming through the greenhouse effect, which prevents the escape of radiant heat from Earth's atmosphere

gas invernadero
gas, por lo general a base de carbono, que contribuye al calentamiento global mediante el efecto invernadero, el cual impide que el calor radiante salga de la atmósfera terrestre

groundwater
water stored below Earth's surface in soil and rock layers

agua subterránea
agua almacenada por debajo de la superficie de la tierra, en capas de suelo y rocas

H

heat
the transfer of thermal energy

calor
transferencia de energía térmica

hertz
measurement of wave frequency

hercio
medida de la frecuencia de onda

hydrogen
the chemical element consisting of one proton and one electron

hidrógeno
elemento químico que consiste en uno o más protones y un electrón

I

infrared electromagnetic energy that has a lower frequency than visible light and is beyond the color of red on the light spectrum: Infrared light is invisible to humans	**infrarrojo** energía electromagnética que tiene una frecuencia menor que la luz visible y que está más allá del color rojo en el espectro de luz: la luz infrarroja es invisible para los seres humanos
inherit to receive genetic information and traits from a parent or parents (related word: inheritance)	**heredar** recibir información y rasgos genéticos de un padre o de los padres (palabra relacionada: herencia)
interference the effect of two or more waves traveling through the same medium	**interferencia** efecto de dos o más ondas que viajan por el mismo medio

keystone species within the ecological community, this species has a critical role in maintaining the structure of the community	**especies clave** dentro de la comunidad ecológica, estas especies tienen un papel crucial en el mantenimiento de la estructura de la comunidad
kinetic energy the energy an object has due to its motion	**energía cinética** energía que tiene un objeto debido a su movimiento
kinetic friction a resistive force between two objects moving pass each other	**fricción cinética** fuerza de resistencia entre dos objetos que se mueven uno sobre el otro
Kuiper Belt an area in the solar system beyond the planets where many small, icy bodies are located	**Cinturón de Kuiper** área del sistema solar que se encuentra más allá de los planetas, donde se ubican muchos cuerpos pequeños y helados

L

latitude
angular distance north and south of the equator

latitud
distancia angular al norte y sur del ecuador

light
waves of electromagnetic energy; electromagnetic energy that people can see

luz
ondas de energía electromagnéticas; energía electromagnética que la gente puede ver

light year
the distance light travels in a vacuum in one year; about 6 trillion miles

año luz
distancia que viaja la luz en el espacio en un año; alrededor de 6 billones de millas

liquid
a state of matter with a defined volume but no defined shape and whose molecules roll past each other

líquido
estado de la materia con un volumen definido pero sin forma definida y cuyas moléculas se deslizan unas sobre otras

longitudinal waves
a wave that occurs when the particles of a medium move parallel to the direction of the wave

onda longitudinal
onda que se produce cuando las partículas de un medio se mueven en paralelo a la dirección de la onda

M

magnet
an object with a north and south pole that produces a magnetic field
(related term: magnetism, magnetic)

imán
objeto con un polo norte y un polo sur que produce un campo magnético
(palabra relacionada: magnetismo, magnético)

magnetic field
a region in space near a magnet or electric current in which magnetic forces can be detected

campo magnético
región en el espacio cerca de un imán o de una corriente eléctrica, donde pueden detectarse fuerzas magnéticas

magnify
to make something appear larger, usually by using one or more lenses

ampliar
hacer que algo parezca más grande, generalmente usando una o más lentes

---

magnitude
size of ground movement caused by seismic waves due to energy released

magnitud
tamaño del movimiento de la tierra provocado por las ondas sísmicas debido a la energía liberada

---

mangrove
tree that grows in tidal zones

manglar
árbol que crece en zonas costeras

---

mass
the amount of matter in an object

masa
cantidad de materia en un objeto

---

matter
material that has mass and takes up some amount of space

materia
material que tiene masa y ocupa espacio

---

measure
to use a tool to learn more about the volume, length or weight of an object
(related word: measurement)

medir
usar una herramienta para saber más sobre el volumen, la longitud o el peso de un objeto
(palabra relacionada: medición)

---

meteor
a streak of light in the sky that forms when a piece of rock from space burns up in Earth's atmosphere (related term: shooting star)

meteoro
reflejo de luz en el cielo que se forma cuando una pieza de roca del espacio se quema en la atmósfera de la Tierra
(palabra relacionada: estrella fugaz)

---

mold
a fossil that forms when the remains of an organism leave an imprint in the sediment after the organic material has been completely replaced

molde
fósil que se forma cuando los restos de un organismo dejan una impresión en el sedimento después de que el material orgánico haya sido remplazado completamente

moon
a body in outer space that orbits a planet; a natural satellite

luna
cuerpo en el espacio exterior que orbita alrededor de un planeta; satélite natural

---

motion
a change in the position of an object compared to another object
(related term: move, movement)

movimiento
cambio en la posición de un objeto en comparación con otro objeto
(palabra relacionada: mover, desplazamiento)

N

nebulae
an interstellar cloud made up of hydrogen gas, plasma, helium gas, and dust

nebulosa
una nube interestelar constituida por gases (hidrógeno y helio), plasma y polvo

---

nebular hypothesis
the theory that a solar system evolves from a hot gaseous nebula

hipótesis nebular
teoría que sostiene que un sistema solar evoluciona a partir de una nebulosa gaseosa caliente

---

Newton's laws
the three fundamental laws Isaac Newton discovered governing the motion of objects

leyes de Newton
las tres leyes fundamentales que Isaac Newton descubrió sobre el movimiento de los objetos

---

nitrogen
an element that makes up most of the air near Earth's surface: nitrogen is a gas at room temperature

nitrógeno
elemento que forma la mayor parte del aire que se encuentra cerca de la superficie de la Tierra: el nitrógeno es un gas a temperatura ambiente

O

offspring
a new organism that is the product of reproduction

descendencia
organismo nuevo que es el producto de la reproducción

optical
having to do with the eye or lenses

óptico
relacionado con los ojos o con las lentes

orbit
the circular path of an object as it revolves around another object

órbita
trayectoria circular de un objeto que se forma a medida que gira alrededor de otro objeto.

organism
any individual living thing

organismo
todo ser vivo individual

outer core
the liquid outer portion of Earth's core, composed primarily of iron and nickel

núcleo externo
parte exterior, líquida, del núcleo de la Tierra, compuesto principalmente por hierro y níquel

oxygen
an element that makes up about 21% of Earth's atmosphere; a gas in Earth's atmosphere and in water that living organisms breathe

oxígeno
elemento que forma aproximadamente el 21% de la atmósfera de la Tierra; gas que se encuentra en la atmósfera de la Tierra y en el agua que los organismos vivos respiran

P

photosynthesis
the process in which plants and some other organisms use the energy in sunlight to make food

fotosíntesis
proceso en el cual las plantas y algunos otros organismos usan la energía del Sol para producir alimentos

planet
a large circular mass that revolves around a star

planeta
gran masa circular que gira alrededor de una estrella

plate tectonics theory
the theory that Earth's crust is made up of individual plates that gradually move in relation to each other

teoría de la tectónica de placas
teoría que dice que la corteza de la Tierra está formada por placas individuales que se mueven gradualmente en relación una con otra

polar
in earth science, having to do with the areas on Earth closest to the geographic North or South poles; in chemistry, describes a molecule that has a positively charged side and a negatively charged side
(related words: pole, polarity)

polar
en la ciencia de la tierra, tiene que ver con las áreas de la Tierra más próximas a los polos geográficos Norte y Sur; en química, describe una molécula que tiene un lado con carga positiva y otro con carga negativa
(palabra relacionada: polo, polaridad)

pole
the opposite ends of a battery, a magnet, or the north and south ends of Earth

polo
extremos opuestos de una batería eléctrica, un imán, o los extremos norte y sur de la Tierra

pollution
harmful materials put into the air, water, or soil at a faster rate than the environment can be cleansed
(related words: pollute, pollutant)

contaminación
materiales perjudiciales que se depositan en el aire, el agua o el suelo a un ritmo más rápido del que se pueden eliminar del ambiente
(palabras relacionadas: contaminar, contaminante)

population
the group of organisms of the same species living in the same area

población
grupo de organismos de la misma especie que viven en la misma área

position
a specific point in space

posición
punto específico en el espacio

potential energy
the amount of energy that is stored in an object; energy that an object has because of its position relative to other objects

energía potencial
cantidad de energía almacenada en un objeto; energía que tiene un objeto debido a su posición relativa con otros objetos

precipitation
water that is released from clouds in the sky; includes rain, snow, sleet, hail, and freezing rain

precipitación
agua liberada de las nubes en el cielo; incluye la lluvia, la nieve, la aguanieve, el granizo y la lluvia congelada

protein
a nutrient used by animals

proteína
nutriente usado por los animales

R

reflect
to strike a surface and bounce back in the opposite direction (related word: reflection)

reflejar
golpear sobre una superficie y rebotar en la dirección opuesta (palabra relacionada: reflexión)

refraction
a change in the direction and velocity which occurs when a seismic or electromagnetic wave travels from one material into another of different density, state, or elasticity

refracción
cambio en la dirección y velocidad que se produce cuando una onda sísmica o una onda electromagnética pasan de un material a otro que tiene diferente densidad, estado o elasticidad

repel
to force an object away or to keep it away (related term: repulsion)

repeler
forzar a un objeto para que se aleje o mantenerlo alejado (término relacionado: repulsión)

revolution
the orbiting of an object around another object

revolución
movimiento por el cual un objeto gira alrededor de otro objeto describiendo una órbita completa

rotate
turning around on an axis; spinning (related word: rotation)

rotar
girar sobre un eje; dar vueltas (palabra relacionada: rotación)

rotation
the spinning of a celestial body, such as a planet, around an axis

rotación
giro de un cuerpo celeste, como un planeta, alrededor de un eje

S

satellite
a natural or artificial object that revolves around another object in space

satélite
objeto natural o artificial que gira alrededor de otro objeto en el espacio

sedimentary rock
a type of rock formed by gravity pressing fragments of other rocks and minerals together as they settle on land or under the ocean over a long period of time

roca sedimentaria
tipo de roca que se forma cuando la gravedad junta los fragmentos de otras rocas y minerales a medida que se asientan en la tierra o debajo del océano, a través de un largo período

---

solar energy
energy that comes from the sun

energía solar
energia que proviene del Sol

---

solar system
a system of objects that revolve around a star

sistema solar
conjunto de objetos que giran alrededor de una estrella

---

solid
matter with a fixed volume and shape

sólido
materia con un volumen y una forma determinada

---

sound
a vibration that travels through a material, such as air or water; something that you sense with your hearing

sonido
vibración que viaja a través de un material, como el aire o el agua; lo que se percibe a través de la audición

---

sound wave
a sound vibration as it is passing through a material: Most sound waves spread out in every direction from their source.

onda sonora
vibración de sonido que se produce cuando se atraviesa un material: La mayoría se dispersa desde la fuente en todas direcciones.

---

space
the large, empty part of the universe that does not contain any matter

espacio
parte vacía y enorme del universo que no contiene ningún tipo de materia

---

species
a group of organisms that share similar characteristics and can mate with each other to produce offspring

especie
grupo de organismos que comparten características similares y que se pueden aparear para generar descendencia

speed distance traveled per unit of time	**rapidez** distancia recorrida por unidad de tiempo
star a massive ball of gas in outer space that gives off heat, light and other forms of radiation	**estrella** bola masiva de gas en el espacio exterior que emite calor, luz y otras formas de radiación
sun any star around which planets revolve	**sol** toda estrella alrededor de la cual giran los planetas
surface the top of an object; the outside of an object; the boundary between two objects or materials	**superficie** parte superior de un objeto; exterior de un objeto; límite entre dos objetos o materiales
sustainable describes a material or resource that is able to meet the demands of current use and yet be maintained in usable quantities to meet indefinite future demands.	**sostenible** describe un material o recurso que es capaz de satisfacer las demandas de uso actual y mantenerse en cantidades utilizables para satisfacer demandas futuras indefinidas
system a group of parts that work together to function or perform a task	**sistema** un grupo de partes que trabajan juntas para funcionar o realizar una tarea

T

telescope an instrument used to observe objects that are far away	**telescopio** instrumento usado para observar objetos que se encuentran alejados
theory of evolution A theory that the various species of living organisms have their origin in common ancestors and that the distinguishable differences are due to heritable modifications in successive generations	**teoría de la evolución** teoría de que varias especies de organismos vivos tienen su origen en antepasados comunes y que las diferencias que se distinguen se deben a modificaciones heredadas en generaciones sucesivas

theory
a set of statements or principles devised to explain a group of facts or phenomena, especially one that has been repeatedly tested or is widely accepted and can be used to make predictions about natural phenomena

teoría
conjunto de declaraciones o principios concebido para explicar un grupo de hechos o fenómenos, especialmente uno repetidamente probado o ampliamente aceptado y que puede usarse para hacer predicciones sobre fenómenos naturales

thrust
a reaction force that pushes an object forward

empuje
fuerza de reacción que impulsa a un objeto hacia adelante

topography
detailed mapping of the physical features of a small locale or area

topografía
características físicas que definen el relieve de un lugar, como montañas, valles y la forma de los accidentes geográficos

trait
a characteristic or property of an organism

rasgo
característica o propiedad de un organismo

translucent
describes materials that allow some light to travel through them, but not enough to see through the material

translúcido
describe materiales que permite que pase algo de luz a través de ellos, pero no lo suficiente como para ver a través del material

transparent
describes materials through which light can travel; materials that can be seen through

transparente
describe materiales a través de los cuales puede viajar la luz; materiales a través de los cuales se puede ver

transverse waves
a wave that occurs when the particles of a medium are displaced perpendicularly to the direction of the wave

onda transversal
onda que se produce cuando las partículas de un medio se mueven perpendicularmente a la dirección de la onda

tundra
extremely cold climate located near the North and South Poles and on the tops of mountains; receives very little precipitation and has no trees

tundra
clima extremadamente frío ubicado cerca de los polos Norte y Sur y en la cima de las montañas; recibe muy pocas precipitaciones y no tiene árboles

U

universe
everything that exists in, on and around Earth

universo
todo lo que existe en, sobre o alrededor de la Tierra

vacuum
an area in which there is no matter

vacío
área donde no hay materia

velocity
the speed and direction of moving objects

velocidad
la rapidez y dirección de objetos en movimiento

vertebrae
the individual bones that stack to form the backbone of an animal
(related word: vertebra)

vértebras
huesos individuales que se apilan para formar la columna vertebral de un animal

vibration
the rapid movement of an object back and forth

vibración
rápido movimiento de un objeto hacia delante y hacia atrás

virus
a sub-microscopic infectious agent that is able to grow or reproduce only within a host cell

virus
agente infeccioso submicroscópico que puede crecer o reproducirse solamente dentro de una célula huésped

W

water a compound made of hydrogen and oxygen	**agua** compuesto formado por hidrógeno y oxígeno
water cycle the continual movement of water between the land, ocean, and the air	**ciclo del agua** movimiento continuo del agua entre la tierra, los océanos y el aire
water vapor the gaseous form of water; produced when water evaporates	**vapor de agua** estado gaseoso del agua; se produce cuando el agua se evapora
wave a disturbance caused by a vibration; Waves travel away from the source that makes them.	**onda** perturbación causada por una vibración que se aleja de la fuente que la forma
wavelength the distance between one peak and the next on a wave	**longitud de onda** distancia entre un pico y otro en una onda
weather the properties of the atmosphere at a given time and location, including temperature, air movement and precipitation	**tiempo atmosférico** propiedades de la atmósfera en un determinado momento y lugar; entre ellas, la temperatura, el movimiento de aire y las precipitaciones
weight the force of gravity on an object	**peso** fuerza de gravedad que se ejerce sobre un objeto
wetland an area of land where there is water on the surface or where the soil is completely filled with water for at least part of the year	**humedal** área de tierra donde hay agua en la superficie o donde el suelo está completamente lleno de agua durante, por lo menos, parte del año

Index

Index

U

V

W